edexcel

Edexcel Award in Statistical Methods

Peter Sherran

ALWAYS LEARNING

PEARSON

Published by Pearson Education Limited, Edinburgh Gate, Harlow, Essex, CM20 2JE.

www.pearsonschoolsandfecolleges.co.uk

Edited by Project One Publishing Solutions, Scotland
Typeset and illustrated by Tech-Set Ltd, Gateshead

First published 2013

17 16 15 14 13
10 9 8 7 6 5 4 3 2 1

British Library Cataloguing in Publication Data
A catalogue record for this book is available from the British Library

ISBN 978 1 446 90329 2

Printed in Slovakia by Neografia

Acknowledgements
Every effort has been made to contact copyright holders of material reproduced in this book. Any omissions will be rectified in subsequent printings if notice is given to the publishers.

Notices

The GCSE links provide references to course books as follows:

AF Edexcel GCSE Mathematics A Foundation Student Book

BF Edexcel GCSE Mathematics B Foundation Student Book

16+ Edexcel GCSE Mathematics 16+ Student Book

S Edexcel GCSE Mathematics Statistics

Contents

Self-assessment chart		**iv**
Chapter 1	**Data**	**1**
1.1	Types of data	1
1.2	Data collection	2
1.3	Criticise questionnaires	7
1.4	Reliability	10
Chapter 2	**Displaying data**	**14**
2.1	Pictograms	14
2.2	Bar charts	16
2.3	Line graphs	18
2.4	Dual bar charts	19
2.5	Two-way tables	21
2.6	Pie charts	23
2.7	Time-series graphs	24
2.8	Scatter graphs	27
2.9	Misleading diagrams	28
Chapter 3	**Calculating with data**	**34**
3.1	Averages and range	34
3.2	Range and mode from a stem and leaf diagram	38
Chapter 4	**Interpreting data**	**44**
4.1	Read and interpret data presented in tables	44
4.2	Interpret charts and graphs	48
4.3	Find totals and modes from frequency tables or diagrams	58
4.4	Describe correlation in scatter graphs	61
4.5	Identify trends in time-series graphs	62
4.6	Compare data	64
4.7	Make comparisons and predictions from data and representations of data	70
Chapter 5	**Probability**	**81**
5.1	Use and interpret a probability scale	81
5.2	Write down theoretical and experimental probabilities	83
5.3	Estimate probabilities from practical situations	86
5.4	Add probabilities	87
5.5	List outcomes	88
Practice Paper		**92**
Answers		**102**

Name .... Class ....

Self-assessment chart

	Needs more practice	Almost there	I'm proficient!	Notes
Chapter 1 Data				
1.1 Types of data	☐	☐	☐	
1.2 Data collection	☐	☐	☐	
1.3 Criticise questionnaires	☐	☐	☐	
1.4 Reliability	☐	☐	☐	
Chapter 2 Displaying data				
2.1 Pictograms	☐	☐	☐	
2.2 Bar charts	☐	☐	☐	
2.3 Line graphs				
2.4 Dual bar charts	☐	☐	☐	
2.5 Two-way tables	☐	☐	☐	
2.6 Pie charts	☐	☐	☐	
2.7 Time-series graphs	☐	☐	☐	
2.8 Scatter graphs				
2.9 Misleading diagrams	☐	☐	☐	
Chapter 3 Calculating with data				
3.1 Averages and range	☐	☐	☐	
3.2 Range and mode from a stem and leaf diagram	☐	☐	☐	
Chapter 4 Interpreting data				
4.1 Read and interpret data presented in tables	☐	☐	☐	
4.2 Interpret charts and graphs	☐	☐	☐	
4.3 Find totals and modes from frequency tables or diagrams	☐	☐	☐	
4.4 Describe correlation in scatter graphs	☐	☐	☐	
4.5 Identify trends in time-series graphs	☐	☐	☐	
4.6 Compare data	☐	☐	☐	
4.7 Make comparisons and prediction from data and representations of data	☐	☐	☐	
Chapter 5 Probability	☐	☐	☐	
5.1 Use and interpret a probability scale	☐	☐	☐	
5.2 Write down theoretical and experimental probabilities	☐	☐	☐	
5.3 Estimate probabilities from practical situations	☐	☐	☐	
5.4 Add probabilities	☐	☐	☐	
5.5 List outcomes	☐	☐	☐	

1.1 Types of data

GCSE LINKS
AF: 3.1 Introduction to data; **BF:** Unit 1 1.1 Introduction to data; **S:** 1.2 Types of data

By the end of this section you will know how to:

* Recognise and describe different types of data

Key points

* **Discrete data** can only take specific values.
* **Continuous data** can take any numerical value in a given range.
* **Categorical data** is described by words rather than numbers.

Guided

1 Match each example of data with its type.

The length of a worm	Categorical
The colour of a car	Discrete
The weight of an apple	Continuous
The number of people who vote in an election	
The types of tree in a forest	
The number of pages in a book	

You should know
Measurement of distance, weight, temperature or time gives continuous data.

Practice

2 A teacher's mark book contains the following categories:

Student names **Homework marks** **Topics covered**

a What type of data are the **Student names**? ....

b What type of data are the **Homework marks**? ....

c What type of data are the **Topics covered**? ....

3 Here is a five-sided spinner.

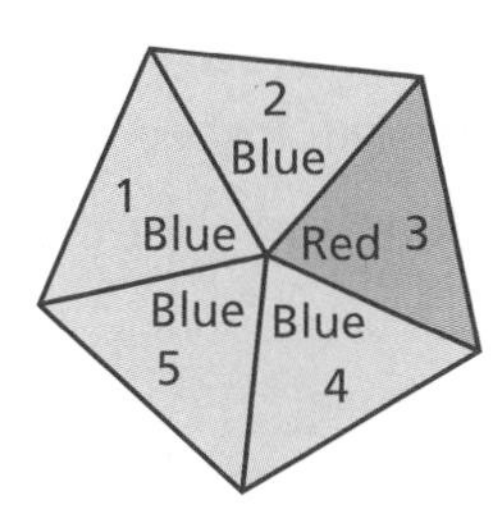

After each spin, Jess records the colour shown and James records the score.

a What type of data does Jess record? ....

b What type of data does James record? ....

4 Jo collects data about different types of butterfly and their wingspans.

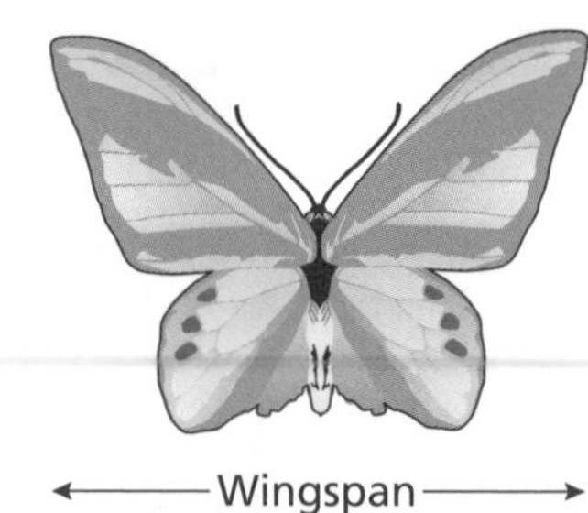

What are the two types of data that Jo collects?

Type of butterfly .... Wingspan ....

5 A six-sided dice is rolled several times.

a Jimmy records the numbers rolled. What kind of data is this? ....

b Diane records whether the numbers rolled are even or odd. What kind of data is this? ....

6 Complete the table by ticking the correct box in each row.

	Data type		
Data	**Categorical**	**Discrete**	**Continuous**
The temperature inside an oven			
The number of sweets in a jar			
The time taken to toast some bread			
The colour of a tin of paint			
The number of days in a month			

Needs more practice ☐ Almost there ☐ I'm proficient! ☐

1.2 Data collection

By the end of this section you will know how to:

* Design and use a data collection sheet for discrete or continuous data

GCSE LINKS
AF: 3.2 Collecting data; **BF:** Unit 1 1.2 Collecting data; **16+:** 19.1 Designing and using data collection sheets; **S:** 1.9 Collecting data

Key points

* A simple **data collection sheet** has a **data column**, a **tally column** and a **frequency column**. The frequency column is where you put the **totals** of the tally marks.
* **Discrete data** may be shown as a list of values in the data column.
* **Discrete data** may be grouped into class intervals in the data column.
* **Continuous data** is always grouped into **class intervals** in the data column. A class interval contains the numbers between its end-points.

Guided

1 A dice is rolled 60 times. The numbers rolled are shown below.

4	3	3	2	6	4	1	3	5	6	1	4
6	5	5	4	1	3	6	2	2	2	5	6
3	1	1	3	5	4	5	2	3	4	1	6
2	5	3	6	4	4	5	5	5	6	1	2
3	3	2	1	6	5	6	3	2	4	1	1

a Complete the data collection sheet to show this data.

Number rolled	Tally	Frequency
1	||	
2	|	
3	|||	
4	|||	
5	|	
6	||	

Remember this
In the tally, use 𝍸 to stand for 5.

Hint
It's a good idea to cross off data values as you put them in the tally to make sure you don't miss any values out or repeat them.

You should know
Once the tally marks have been entered, count them to give the frequency for each number rolled.

b Find the total of the numbers in the **Frequency** column.

Total = ...

c Explain how your answer to part **b** may be used to check your answer to part **a**.

....

....

2 At a charity event, people were asked to guess the number of balloons inside a car. The results are shown below.

387	410	306	425	450	386	390	421	480	395
367	409	465	382	340	375	400	420	478	365
391	372	408	450	432	387	324	305	376	428
387	361	472	436	424	381	379	401	432	360
427	348	375	429	460	384				

a Complete the data collection sheet to show this data.

Guess	Tally	Frequency
301–330	|	
331–360		
361–390	|||	
391–420	||	
421–450	|||	
451–480	|	

Hint
There are too many different values to list them all in the table. It is better to group the values into class intervals instead.

Remember this
301–330 is one class interval. This data is grouped into six class intervals.

b How many people tried to guess the number of balloons?

....

3 The heights of 30 students in Year 11 were measured.
The results (in metres) are shown below.

~~1.78~~	~~1.69~~	~~1.83~~	~~1.74~~	~~1.85~~	~~1.93~~	~~1.76~~	~~1.65~~	~~1.69~~	~~1.74~~
1.82	1.91	1.87	1.72	1.92	1.86	1.75	1.63	1.70	1.86
1.65	1.76	1.82	1.89	1.78	1.72	1.84	1.79	1.68	1.82

Complete the data collection sheet to show this data.

Height (h m)	Tally	Frequency
$1.60 < h \leqslant 1.65$		
$1.65 < h \leqslant 1.70$	||	
$1.70 < h \leqslant 1.75$	||	
$1.75 < h \leqslant$	||	
$1.80 < h \leqslant 1.85$	||	
.... $< h \leqslant 1.90$	|	
.... $< h \leqslant 1.95$	|	

You should know
The class $1.65 < h \leqslant 1.70$ includes 1.70 but not 1.65.

4 This spinner is spun 40 times. The results are shown below.

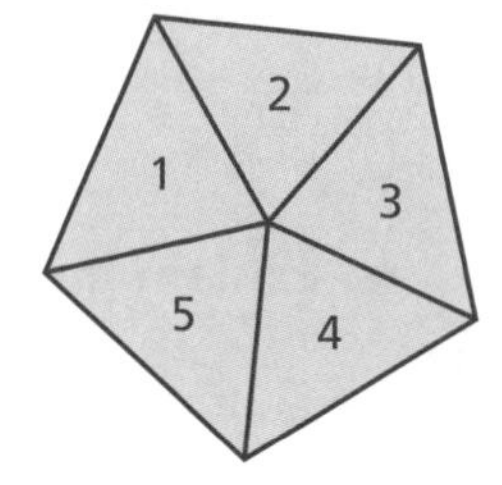

4	3	3	5	2	4	1	2	5	1
5	3	2	2	1	4	5	1	4	3
5	1	1	2	3	2	4	2	5	4
4	2	2	4	2	1	5	3	3	5

a Complete this data collection sheet for the spinner.

Number spun	Tally	Frequency

b Which number has the highest frequency? ....

5 30 students were asked to keep track of the number of text messages that they sent in one week.
The results are shown below.

72	91	45	136	28	15	184	102	123	87
36	175	64	83	89	72	134	128	75	192
88	46	22	16	165	34	173	109	86	21

a Complete this data collection sheet for the numbers of texts sent.

Number of texts	Tally	Frequency
11–40		
41–80		
81–110		
111–150		
151–200		

You should know
The classes do not have to be the same width.

b Explain why it is sensible to group the data in this case.

....

....

....

c How many students sent more than 150 texts? ....

6 A biology student measures the lengths, in cm, of some leaves from an oak tree. Her data is shown below.

14.2	18.6	13.3	17.5	12.8	16.4	18.1	19.6	17.8	16.4
12.9	19.7	17.6	19.3	14.8	16.5	14.9	15.3	12.8	18.2
15.7	18.3	19.4	18.7	17.9	14.5	16.2	13.8	19.8	16.6

Hint

Start with the class interval $12.0 < l \leqslant 13.0$, where l represents length.

Design and complete a data collection sheet for this data.

7 The numbers of goals scored in a sample of 40 Premier League football games are shown below.

2	0	1	0	4	2	0	3	1	2
1	1	2	1	3	2	5	1	2	3
2	0	4	2	1	1	4	3	2	0
6	3	0	0	2	1	2	4	1	2

Design and complete a data collection sheet for this data.

8 Sean wants to find the most popular television programmes from the list below.

American Idol	Bear Grylls	Coronation Street
EastEnders	Master Chef	Modern Family
QI	The Love Machine	The X-Factor

He is going to use a data collection sheet.

a Design a data collection sheet that Sean might use.

b What type of data is Sean planning to collect? ....

9 a The shoe sizes of a class of Y11 students are shown below.

$8\frac{1}{2}$	11	6	$7\frac{1}{2}$	$6\frac{1}{2}$	7	10	9	$9\frac{1}{2}$	10
9	$5\frac{1}{2}$	6	$8\frac{1}{2}$	9	10	7	6	5	8
11	9	6	$5\frac{1}{2}$	6	10				

Complete this data collection sheet for the data.

Shoe size	Tally	Frequency
$5–5\frac{1}{2}$		
$6–6\frac{1}{2}$		

b What type of data is this? ....

Needs more practice ☐ Almost there ☐ I'm proficient! ☐

1.3 Criticise questionnaires

By the end of this section you will know how to:

* Recognise common errors in questions written for questionnaires

GCSE LINKS
AF: 3.3 Questionnaires; **BF:** Unit 1 1.3 Questionnaires; **16+:** 19.2 Design and criticise questions for questionnaires; **S:** 1.9 Collecting data

Key points

* A **questionnaire** is a set of questions designed to **collect data** for a particular purpose.
* A **biased** question is one that suggests a particular response.
* Avoid any **bias** in the questions.
* Make sure the questions are clear and easily understood.
* Do not include questions that may embarrass the person being asked.
* Allow for the full range of responses.
* Do not ask questions that are too difficult.

Guided

1 Here are some questions that are not suitable for a questionnaire.
For each one, give a reason why the question is unsuitable.

a The people of this town do not want a new supermarket.
Do you agree?

☐ Yes ☐ No ☐ Undecided

Remember this
There should be no hint of what the expected answer is.

....

....

b How much do you earn in a year?

☐ More than £60 000 ☐ £50 000–£60 000
☐ £40 000–£49 999 ☐ Less than £40 000

Hint
Imagine that you earn £7000 per year.

....

....

c How often do you travel by train?

☐ All the time ☐ Quite often
☐ Sometimes ☐ Not very often

Hint
Are you clear about the choices? What do they mean?

....

....

d How many books do you read in a month?

☐ 0–5 ☐ 5–10
☐ 10–15 ☐ More than 15

Hint
How would you answer this? What if you read 10 books?

....

....

Practice

2 Say what you think is wrong with these questionnaire questions.

a Are you in favour of a new road that will cut through the beautiful countryside?

☐ Yes ☐ No ☐ Not sure

....

....

b How many times a week do you eat meat?

☐ 1–2 ☐ 3–4 ☐ 5 or more

....

....

c How many hours of television do you watch on a typical day?

☐ 0–1 ☐ 1–2 ☐ 2–3 ☐ 3–4 ☐ More than 4

....

....

d What do you think is wrong with the new lunch menu?

☐ Not enough choice ☐ Too expensive ☐ Too repetitive ☐ Other

....

....

e How many times have you been to the cinema in the last 5 years?

☐ 0–5 ☐ 6–10 ☐ 11–15 ☐ 16–20 ☐ More than 20

....

....

f Do you agree that the tuck-shop should be open before school starts?

☐ Yes ☐ No ☐ Not sure

....

....

Guided

3 Rewrite each of the following questions to make them suitable for a questionnaire.

a Do you agree that students should be able to use the computer room at lunchtime?

☐ Yes ☐ No ☐ Don't know

Do you agree or .... that students should be able to use the computer room at lunchtime?

☐ Agree ☐ .... ☐ Don't know

b Which of these meals is your favourite?

☐ Salad ☐ Fish and chips ☐ A pasta dish ☐ Curry

Which of these meals would you ....?

☐ Salad ☐ Fish and chips ☐ A pasta dish ☐ Curry ☐ .... of these

c How much time do you usually spend on homework in a week?

☐ 0–3 hours ☐ 3–6 hours ☐ 6–9 hours

How much time do you usually spend on homework in a week?

☐ 0–3 hours ☐ 4–6 hours ☐ .... hours ☐ more than .... hours

d Do you think that revision guides are helpful?

☐ Yes ☐ No

Do you think that revision guides are helpful?

☐ Yes ☐ No ☐ ....

Practice

4 Say what you think is wrong with these questionnaire questions.

a How many hours sleep do you get each night?

☐ Less than 5 ☐ 5 or 6 ☐ 6 or 7 ☐ More than 7

....

....

b How many calories are in the food you eat on average per day?

☐ Less than 1800 ☐ 1800–1999 ☐ 2000–2200 ☐ More than 2200

....

....

c Do you agree that eating too many crisps will make you gain weight?

☐ Yes ☐ No ☐ Don't know

....

....

GCSE

5 Rewrite each of the following questions to make them suitable for a questionnaire.

a How tall are you?

☐ Less than 1.5 m ☐ 1.5 m–1.7 m ☐ 1.7 m to 6 feet ☐ More than 6 feet

....

....

....

....

b How do you feel about the proposal that the school has a new navy blue uniform?

☐ Strongly agree ☐ Agree ☐ Don't know

....

....

....

....

6 In 2013 the Scottish Government proposed the following question for a referendum on Scottish independence:

Do you agree that Scotland should be an independent country?

Yes ☐

No ☐

The Electoral Commission advised that the question was biased.
The advice was accepted and the question was rewritten.

a Explain why the original question was biased.

....

....

b Rewrite the question so that it is fair.

....

....

....

....

Needs more practice ☐ Almost there ☐ I'm proficient! ☐

1.4 Reliability

By the end of this section you will know how to:

* Decide whether a survey or questionnaire will produce reliable information

GCSE LINKS
AF: 3.4 Sampling;
BF: Unit 1 1.4 Sampling;
S: 1.6 Populations and sampling

Key points

* A survey or questionnaire is **reliable** if the data it produces **accurately** represents the views of the people involved.
* Avoid any bias in the questions.
* Avoid bias by choosing a **random sample** of people to answer the questions.
* Choose a sample large enough to represent the target group.
* Choose a sample small enough to be manageable.

Guided

1 A town council is considering closing the library in the town centre on Wednesday afternoons to save money. They conduct a survey of 100 people to test the views of people in the town. The survey is done outside the library on a Wednesday afternoon.
Explain why the results will not be reliable.

Hint
Do you think the sample chosen will fairly represent the views of the town?

....

....

....

....

....

2 The head of English wants to know about the popularity of English across the school. She asks the pupils in her Year 7 top set to vote for their favourite subject. Do you think the results will be reliable? Give your reasons.

Hint
Do you think that there is any bias in the way that the sample was chosen?

....

....

....

....

....

3 The editor of a newspaper wants to predict the result of a local election. He asks 10 people from his office how they will vote. How reliable do you think this method is? Explain your answer.

Hint
Think about bias and also the number of people asked.

....

....

....

....

....

4 A survey was designed to find if people thought it would be a good idea to have a new fitness centre in a town. The survey was carried out on a Monday morning on the High Street between 10 am and 11 am.
Comment on the reliability of the survey.

....

....

....

....

....

5 A survey was carried out to see if householders were happy with the refuse collection service. An area of the town was chosen at random and people from that area took part in the survey. Explain why the results of the survey may not be reliable.

....

....

....

....

....

Step into GCSE

6 A survey is carried out to find the most popular spectator sport in a city.
The views of 100 people are taken between 1 pm and 2 pm on a Saturday.

a Explain why the results of the survey may be unreliable.

....

....

....

....

....

b Describe the changes you would introduce to make the survey more reliable.

....

....

....

....

....

Don't forget!

- Discrete data can only take .... values.
- Continuous data can take any .... value in a given ....
- Categorical data is described by .... rather than ....
- On a data collection sheet, continuous data is always .... into .... intervals.
- A questionnaire is a set of .... designed to collect data for ....
- A biased question is one that suggests a particular ....
- Allow for the full .... of responses.
- A survey or questionnaire is reliable if the data it produces .... the views of the people involved.
- Avoid bias by choosing a .... of people to answer the questions.

Exam-style questions

1 Suki lives near a main road. She decides to do a survey of the first 50 vehicles that pass by her house. Her results are shown below.

Car	Car	Truck	Car	Car	Truck	Van	Van	Car	Truck
Car	Van	Car	Car	Bus	Car	Van	Car	Car	Van
Car	M/bike	M/bike	Car	Van	Truck	Truck	Van	Car	Car
Van	Car	Car	Truck	Car	Car	Truck	Truck	Van	Car
Car	Bus	Truck	Car	Car	Car	Car	Car	Car	Van

a Design and complete a data collection sheet for Suki's data.

b What kind of data has Suki collected? ....

2 Some Year 11 students want to measure the support for the idea that they should always be allowed an early lunch. They use the following question in a questionnaire.

> Do you agree that Year 11 students should always be in the first sitting for lunch?
>
> ☐ Yes ☐ No ☐ Don't know

Rewrite the question to make it more suitable.

....

....

....

....

....

3 Sundeep wants to know how many magazines people read.
He uses the following question in a questionnaire.

> How many magazines do you read?
>
> ☐ 1–2 ☐ 2–3 ☐ 3–4

Write down **three** things wrong with this question.

1 ....

2 ....

3 ....

Pictograms

By the end of this section you will know how to:

* Draw pictograms

GCSE LINKS
AF: 12.1 Pictograms; **BF:** Unit 1 2.1 Pictograms; **S:** 2.8 Pictograms

Key points

* A **pictogram** uses symbols or pictures to represent numbers of items or events.
* A pictogram should have a **title**.
* A pictogram should have a **key** showing the value of each symbol.
* **Fractions** of a symbol may be used for smaller amounts. Choose a symbol that is easily divided into smaller parts that can be understood.

Guided

1 The table shows the numbers of people attending a school production during one week. Each figure has been rounded to the nearest 10.

Day	Number of people
Monday	120
Tuesday	90
Wednesday	100
Thursday	80
Friday	130
Saturday	150

Complete the pictogram to show this data.

Pictogram showing people attending the school production

Monday	☺☺☺☺☺☺☺☺☺☺☺☺
Tuesday	☺☺☺☺☺☺☺☺☺
Wednesday	
Thursday	
Friday	
Saturday	

Key: ☺ represents 10 people

Hint
For Monday:
120 ÷ 10 = 12 so use 12 symbols.

Remember this
Draw the symbols the same size and keep them evenly spaced.

2 Show how to represent the following numbers using the key shown.

Key: ⊞ represents 4 boxes

a 6 boxes

b 7 boxes ....

c 10 boxes ....

d 13 boxes ....

Practice

3 Jamie owns a busy restaurant.
He records the number of customers at different times on a Saturday night.
The table shows his results.

Time	Number of customers
7 pm	24
8 pm	38
9 pm	46
10 pm	32
11 pm	27

Hint
Calculate the number of symbols needed for each time before you draw the pictogram.

Show Jamie's data on a pictogram using the key shown.

Key: ⊕ represents 4 customers

GCSE

4 The table shows the number of letters received by a company each day for a week.

Day	Number of letters
Monday	17
Tuesday	12
Wednesday	15
Thursday	11
Friday	14

Using the data shown in the pictogram for Monday, work out and complete the key.
Complete the pictogram.

Day	Number of letters received
Monday	☐ ☐ ☐ ☐ ☐ ☐ ☐ ☐ ▯
Tuesday	
Wednesday	
Thursday	
Friday	

Key: ☐ represents .... letters

Hint
8.5 rectangles are used here for 17 letters.

Bar charts

GCSE LINKS
AF: 12.3 Bar charts;
BF: Unit 1 2.3 Bar charts;
S: 2.9 Bar charts

By the end of this section you will know how to:

* Draw bar charts

Key points

* The **height** or **length** of each bar shows the **value represented**.
* The bars may be horizontal or vertical.
* There should be a gap between the bars.
* The bars should all be the same width.
* The axes on a bar chart should be clearly labelled.

Guided

1 Jess has a jar of sweets with coloured wrappers.
She counts the number of each colour and draws a frequency table.

Colour	Red	Blue	Green	Orange	Purple
Frequency	7	8	5	3	9

Complete the bar chart using the data and write a title.

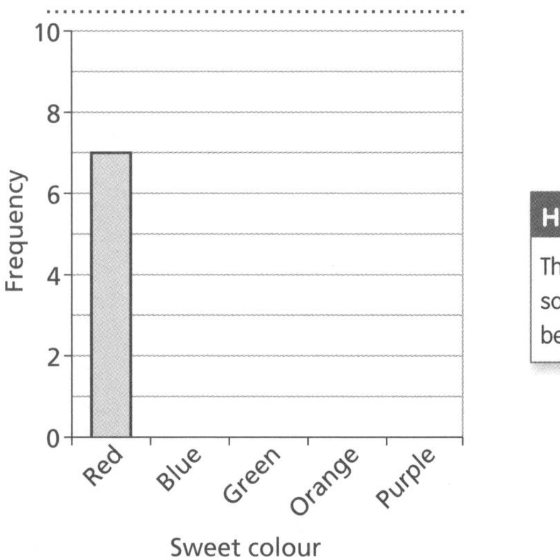

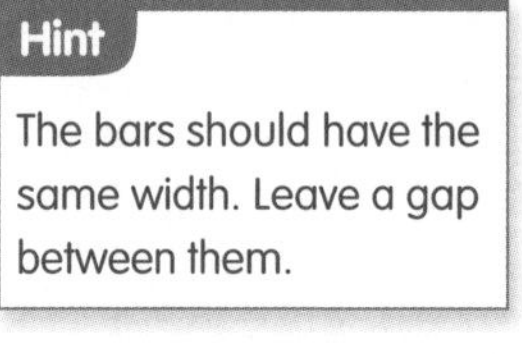

2 Fill in the missing values in these tables.

a Jimmy has 34 marbles of different colours as shown in the table.

Colour	Blue	Green	Yellow	Red
Frequency	8	3	9	....

Hint
When you add the frequency values the total must match the total number of marbles (34).

b The table shows how Jo spent her wages.

Item	Rent	Food	Clothes	Entertainment	Other
Percentage	28	24	16	21	....

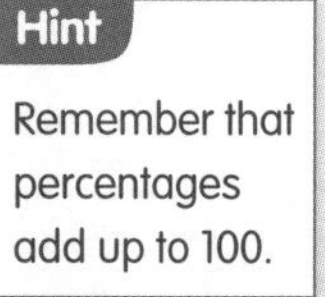

Practice

3 Forty people were asked about their favourite type of television programme. The results are shown in the table.

Programme	Comedy	Drama	Soap	Film	Documentary
Frequency	11	6	10		4

Complete the table and bar chart.

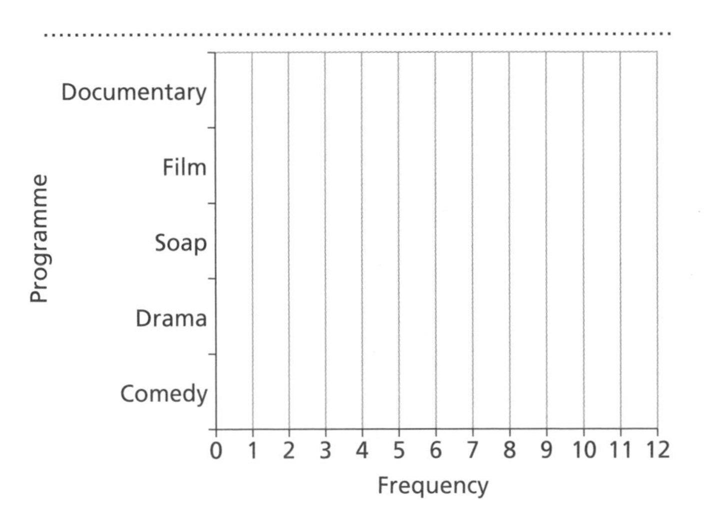

GCSE

4 The pictogram shows how many coins of each type John has saved.

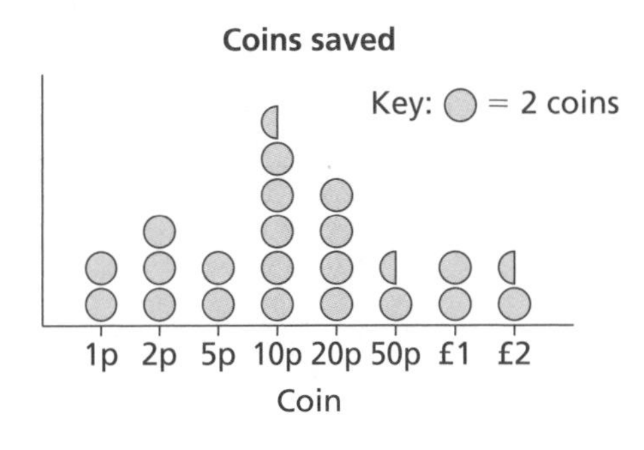

Draw a bar chart to represent the same information.

Needs more practice ☐ Almost there ☐ I'm proficient! ☐

2.3 Line graphs

By the end of this section you will know how to:

* Draw line graphs

GCSE LINKS
AF: 25.1 Drawing and using line graphs; **BF:** Unit 1 4.3 Drawing and using line graphs; **16+:** 22.1 Drawing and using line graphs and scatter graphs; **S:** 6.1 Line graphs

Key points

* A **line graph** is used to display pairs of data values by plotting them as coordinates.
* Points between the plotted points may have no meaning.
* The plotted points are joined with straight lines.

Guided

1 Kate recorded the number of hours of sunshine each day of her holiday.
Her results are shown in the table.

Day	Sat	Sun	Mon	Tue	Wed	Thu	Fri
Hours of sunshine	4	1	6	8	5	4	7

On the grid, draw a line graph for this information.

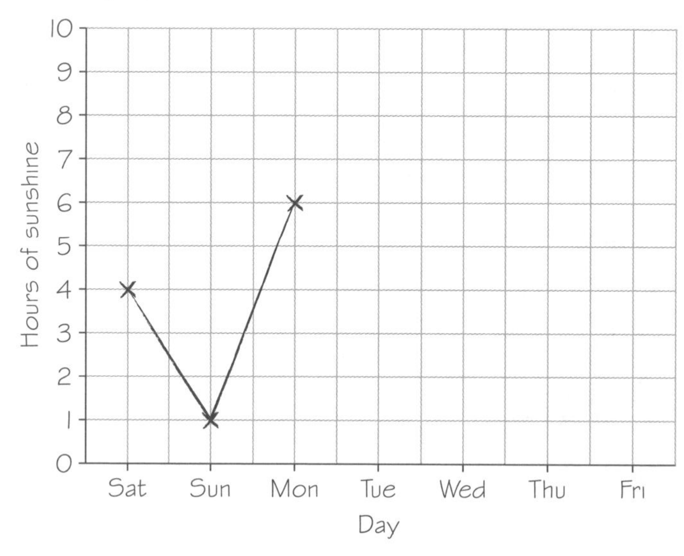

Hint
The first three points have been plotted for you. Each point is joined to the next with a straight line.

Practice

2 A campsite has tents of different sizes for different numbers of people. The table shows how many tents of different sizes are used one night.

Tent size (number of people in tent)	1	2	3	4	5
Frequency	5	12	15	20	16

Draw a line graph for this data.

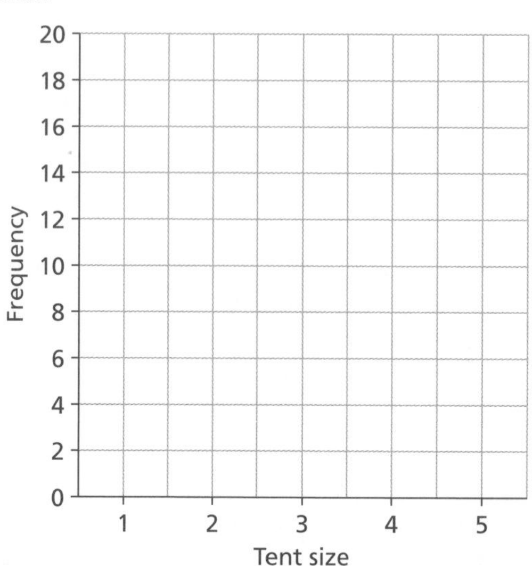

3 Jim checked his pulse rate, in beats per minute (bpm), every 10 minutes during a workout. The table shows his results.

Time (minutes)	Pulse rate (bpm)
0	68
10	157
20	126
30	110
40	145
50	128
60	96

On the grid, draw a line graph to show the information in the table.

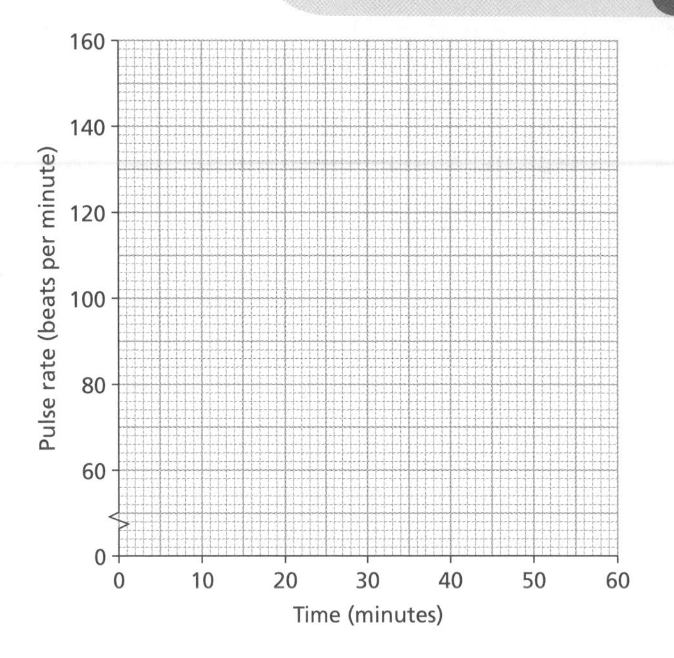

Needs more practice ☐ Almost there ☐ I'm proficient! ☐

2.4 Dual bar charts

By the end of this section you will know how to:

* Draw dual bar charts

GCSE LINKS

AF: 12.4 Comparative and composite bar charts; **BF:** Unit 1 2.4 Comparative and composite bar charts; **16+:** 21.3 Construct and interpret dual and composite bar charts; **S:** 2.15 Using bar charts to make comparisons

Key points

* The bars are **grouped** next to each other in every category.
* The grouping of the bars allows **comparisons** to be made within a category.
* There is a gap between one group of bars and the next.
* The bars may be **horizontal** or **vertical**.
* A dual bar chart should have a key explaining the different bars.

Guided

1 In the run-up to the end-of-course exams a teacher gives his class five tests. For each one, he records the highest and lowest scores for the class. The table shows the results.

Test	1	2	3	4	5
Highest	73	77	76	82	88
Lowest	36	45	40	53	64

Draw a dual bar chart to show the test results.

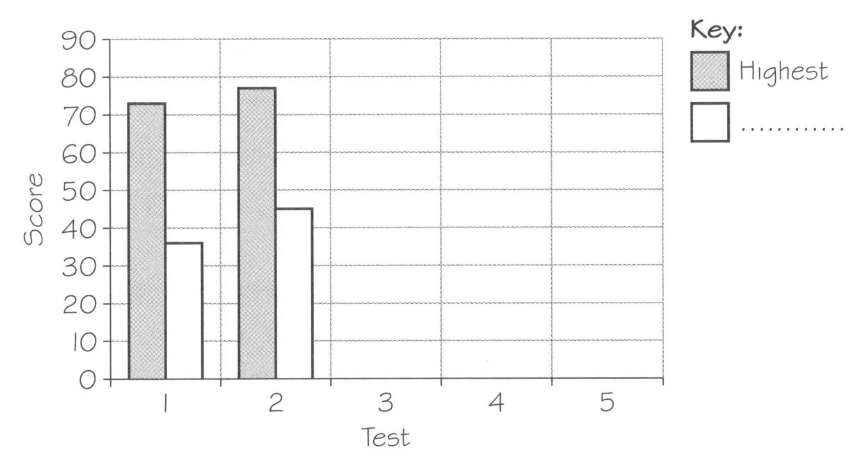

2 A supermarket sells tubs of ice cream in two flavours, vanilla and chocolate.
The table shows how many of each flavour were sold in one week.

Day	Mon	Tue	Wed	Thu	Fri
Vanilla	12	14	10	9	18
Chocolate	11	12	14	7	21

Draw a vertical dual bar chart to show this data.

3 A mixed group of boys and girls were asked to name their favourite sports.
The results are shown in the table.

Sport	Football	Hockey	Tennis	Swimming	Athletics
Boys	10	1	1	2	3
Girls	4	4	3	5	3

Draw a horizontal dual bar chart to show these results.

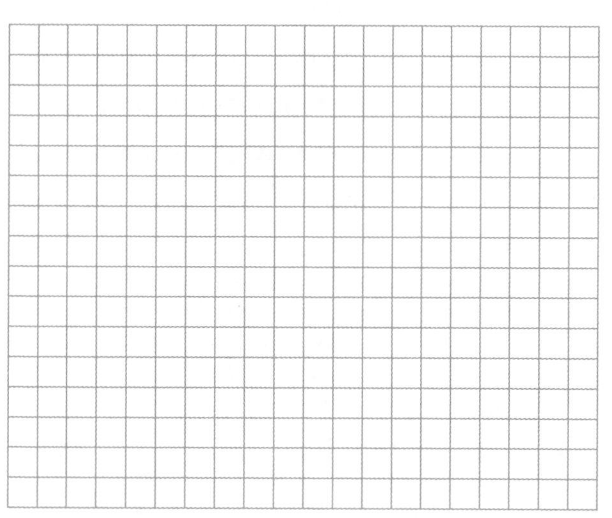

4 A theme park has rides for adults and children. The table shows the numbers of adult and child tickets sold during one week to the nearest 100.

Day	Mon	Tue	Wed	Thu	Fri	Sat	Sun
Adult	2100	1800	1900	2400	2800	3400	3100
Child	2800	2200	2300	3100	3600	4900	4600

Show this information on a dual bar chart.
Use the grid on the opposite page.

Needs more practice ☐ Almost there ☐ I'm proficient! ☐

2.5 Two-way tables

By the end of this section you will know how to:

* Draw two-way tables

GCSE LINKS
AF: 3.5 Two-way and other tables; **BF:** Unit 1 1.5 Two-way and other tables; **16+:** 19.3 Designing and using two-way tables; **S:** 2.5 Two-way tables

Key points

* A **two-way table** has **labelled rows** and **columns**.
* Every number is in a row and a column so it shows **two types of information**.
* The total of all of the rows is equal to the total of all of the columns.

Guided

1 Some Year 11 students were asked which subjects they would like to study in the sixth form. Their responses are shown below.

Boys

Maths	Phys	Chem	Biol	Biol	Maths	Eng	Hist	Geog	~~Art~~	Econ
Geog	Maths	Econ	Phys	Eng	Maths	Biol	Geog	Hist	Hist	Eng

Girls

Eng	Biol	~~Art~~	Maths	Chem	Eng	Biol	Maths	Hist	Geog
Maths	Biol	Econ	Hist	~~Art~~	~~Art~~	Maths	Hist	Eng	Biol

Show this information in a two-way table.

	Art	Biol	Chem	Econ	Eng	Geog	Hist	Maths	Phys	Total
Boys	1									
Girls	3									
Total	4									

Hint
Deal with one subject at a time. Check that the total in the bottom right-hand corner is the same vertically and horizontally.

Practice

2 This two-way table shows the number of students taking languages in the sixth form.

	French	German	Spanish	Total
Boys	7	6	....	18
Girls	8	....	9	24
Total	15	....	....	....

Hint

Use the totals in the rows and columns to find the missing values.

Complete the table.

3 Carol did a survey of favourite pets.
Here are her results.

Boys

dog	dog	cat	fish	rat	dog	rabbit
mouse	hamster	dog	cat	rat	fish	mouse
cat	dog	hamster	dog	fish	rabbit	dog

Girls

cat	mouse	dog	dog	mouse	rabbit	hamster
dog	rabbit	cat	mouse	rabbit	hamster	dog
cat	hamster	dog	mouse	fish	cat	rabbit

Show Carol's results in a two-way table.

4 In a survey, some Year 11 students were asked what they intended to do the following year.
The two-way table below shows the results.

	Sixth form	College	Work	Total
Boys	24		11	58
Girls		29		
Total	52		27	

Complete the two-way table.

Step into GCSE

5 A maths teacher constructed the following two-way table based on 31 students in her class.

	Did homework	Did not do homework	Total
Did bring equipment	24		
Did not bring equipment			5
Total	25		

Complete the two-way table.

Needs more practice ☐ Almost there ☐ I'm proficient! ☐

Pie charts

By the end of this section you will know how to:

* Draw pie charts

GCSE LINKS
AF: 12.2 Pie charts; **BF:** Unit 1 2.2 Pie charts; **16+:** 21.1 Constructing pie charts; **S:** 2.12 Pie charts

Key points

* A **pie chart** is a **circle** divided into **sectors**.
* Each sector represents a **category** of data.
* The **angle** of a sector represents the **size of the category** compared to the whole.
* A pie chart is useful for **comparing** a small number of categories.

Guided

1 The table shows how a class of 30 students travel to school.

Method of travel	Number of students	Angle of pie chart
Bus	14	12° × 14 = 168°
Car	5	12° × 5 =
Cycle	3	
Walk	8	
Total	30	

360° ÷ 30 = 12°

Hint Calculate the number of degrees that represents each student. Remember there are 360° in a circle.

Complete the table and pie chart.

Hint Check that all the angles add up to 360°.

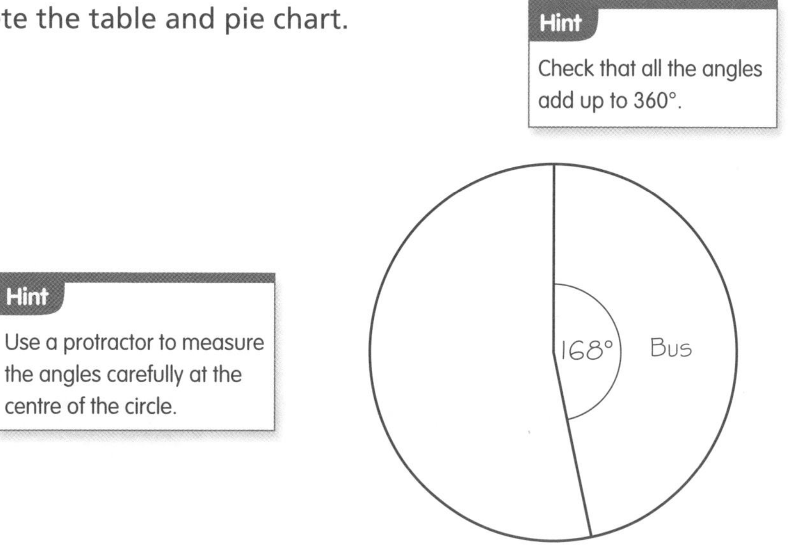

Hint Make sure that you have all the equipment you need for the examination.

Practice

2 A survey of the types of fuel used in 120 cars produced the results shown in the table.

Fuel type	Number of vehicles	Angle of pie chart
Petrol	72	
Diesel	31	
Dual fuel	2	
Hybrid	15	
Total		

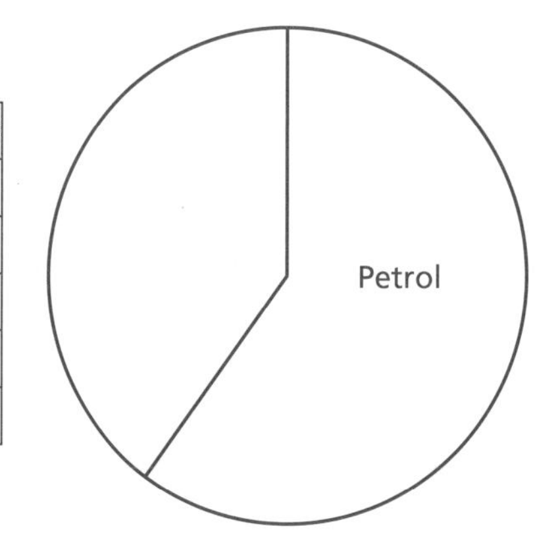

Complete the table and pie chart to show this information.

3 A waste recycling plant separates different types of waste into containers. The table shows the number of containers needed for each type in one month.

Waste type	Number of containers	Angle of pie chart
General waste	30	
Metal	8	
Organic	16	
Paper	6	
Wood	12	
Total		

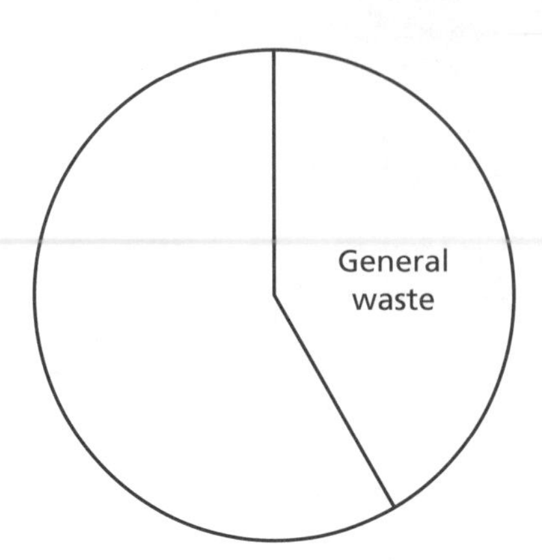

Complete the table and pie chart to show this information.

4 The table below shows how one student spent her day.

Activity	Number of hours	Angle of pie chart
Sleeping	9	
Working	7	
Dining	2	
Relaxing	6	
Total		

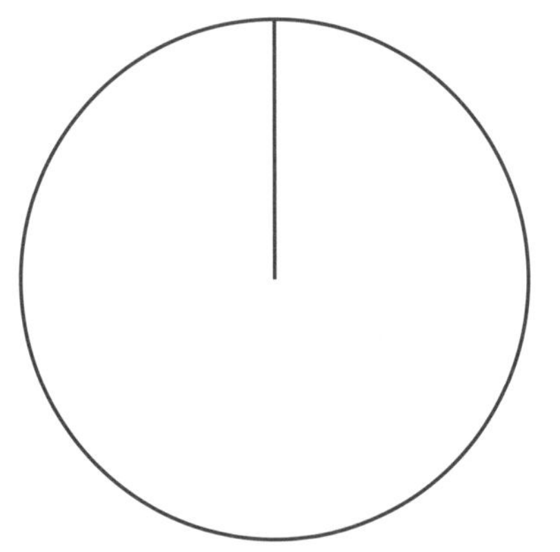

Complete the table and pie chart to show this information.

Step into GCSE

Needs more practice ☐ Almost there ☐ I'm proficient! ☐

2.7 Time-series graphs

GCSE LINKS
S: 6.2 Time series

By the end of this section you will know how to:

* Draw a time-series graph

Key points

* A time-series graph shows how a **quantity** changes over a period of **time**.
* Points are plotted at **equal time intervals**.
* The line segments joining the points should be solid.
* Time is always shown on the **horizontal** axis.

Guided

1 The monthly rainfall at Bridlington was recorded over a 12-month period.
The results are shown in the table.

Month	Jan	Feb	Mar	Apr	May	Jun	Jul	Aug	Sep	Oct	Nov	Dec
Rainfall (mm)	55	38	48	44	51	51	52	66	55	50	60	54

Draw a time-series graph to show this information.

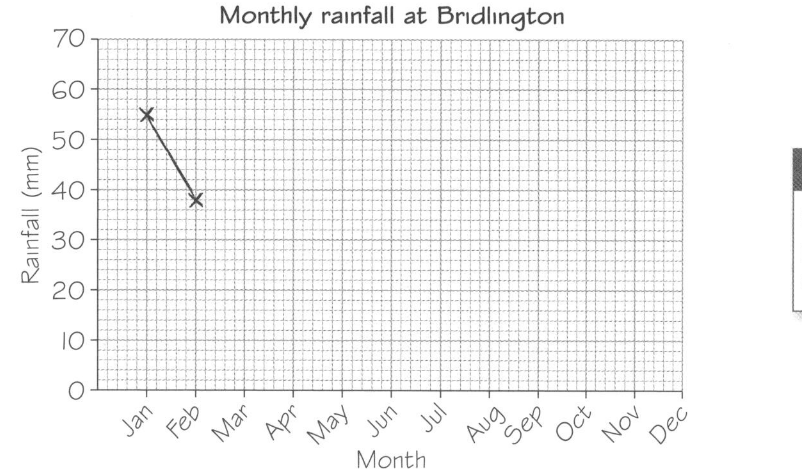

Hint

Plot the remaining points and join them with solid lines.

2 This table shows the quarterly sales of mobile phones from a shop over three years.

	Year											
	2010				2011				2012			
Quarter	1	2	3	4	1	2	3	4	1	2	3	4
Sales (100s)	12	14	15	18	17	19	15	13	15	17	19	22

Draw a time-series graph to show this information.

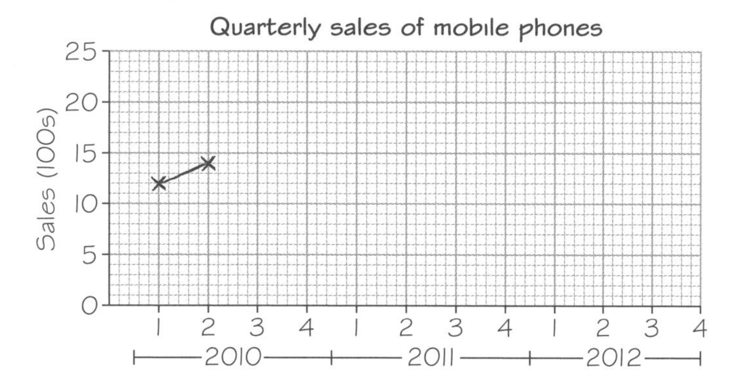

Practice

3 The table shows the numbers of patients treated in the A&E department of a hospital over a two-week period.

	Week 1							**Week 2**						
Day	Mon	Tue	Wed	Thur	Fri	Sat	Sun	Mon	Tue	Wed	Thur	Fri	Sat	Sun
Number of patients	36	31	28	34	45	68	26	32	30	26	33	42	65	22

Draw a time-series graph to show this information.

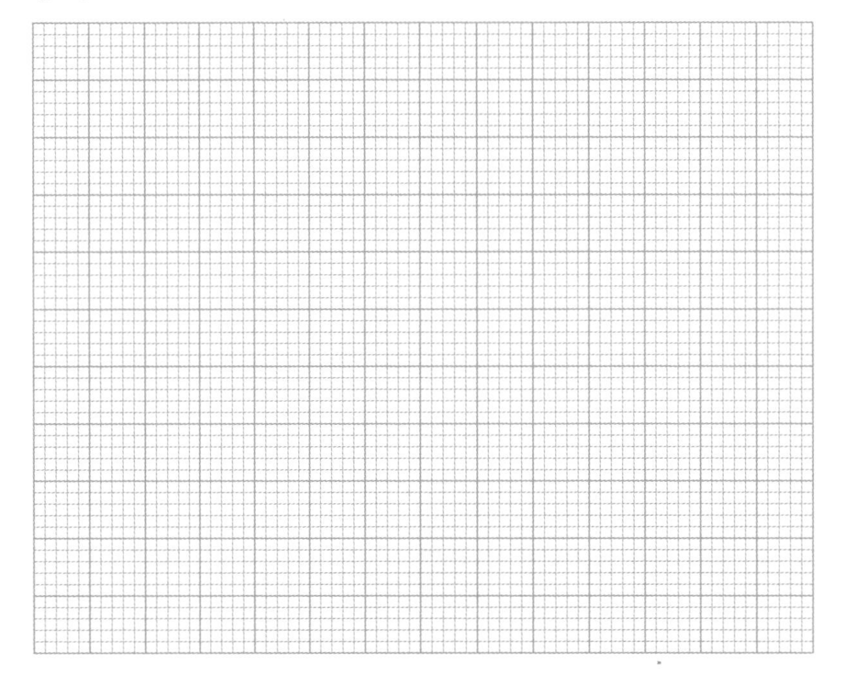

Step into GCSE

4 The table shows how sales of rainwear in the UK varied over a three-year period.

	Year											
	2010				**2011**				**2012**			
Quarter	1	2	3	4	1	2	3	4	1	2	3	4
Sales (£m)	37	31	39	46	41	36	40	53	45	50	40	32

Draw a time-series graph to show this information.

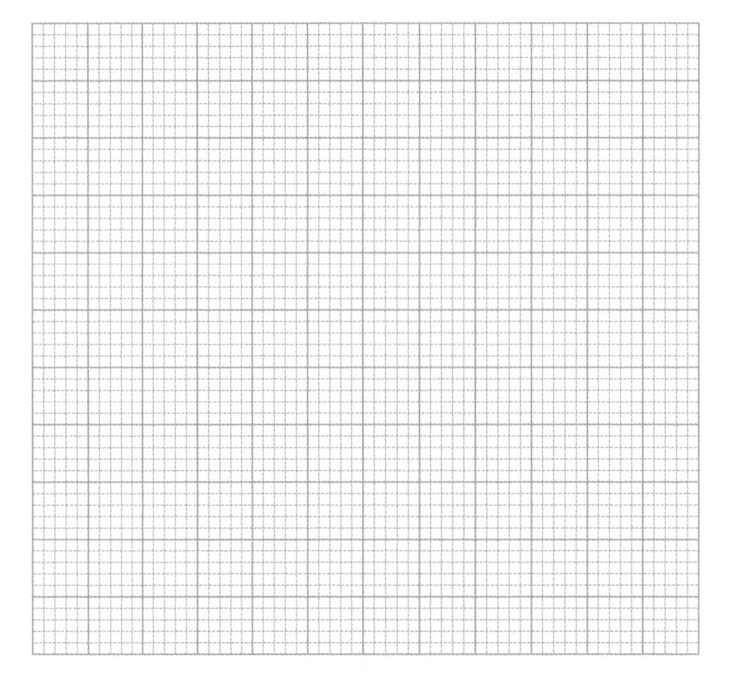

2.8 Scatter graphs

By the end of this section you will know how to:

* Draw scatter graphs

GCSE LINKS
AF: 25.2 Drawing and using scatter graphs; **BF:** Unit 1 4.4 Drawing and using scatter graphs; **16+:** 22.1 Drawing and using line graphs and scatter graphs; **S:** 5.1 Scatter diagrams

Key points

* A **scatter graph** is used to show the **connection** between two variables.
* **Pairs of values** of these variables are plotted as coordinates.
* The pattern of plotted points tells us how the **variables** are **related**.

Guided

1 The table shows the temperature at a UK resort over an 11-day period and the corresponding figure for sales of ice creams.

Temperature (°C)	15	18	19	20	21	25	27	28	30	31	33
Sales (£100s)	6	9	8	11	12	16	20	22	28	27	29

Draw a scatter graph for this data.

Hint
Plot values shown in the table as coordinates.

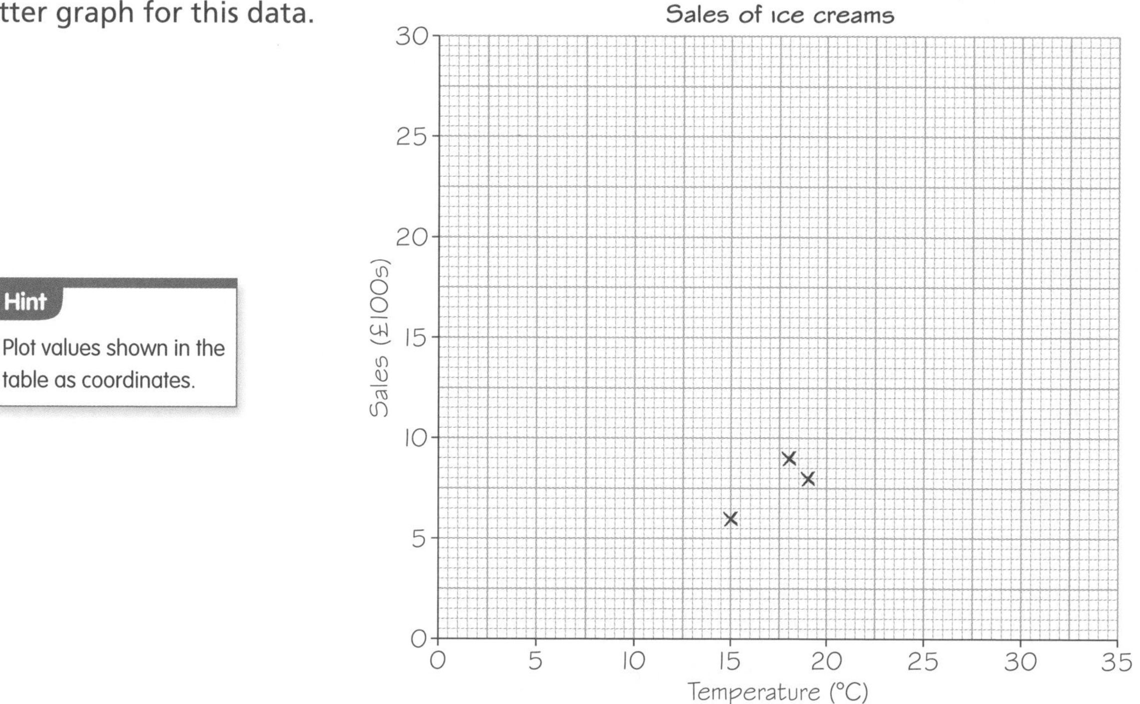

Practice

2 The table shows the maths and physics results for the same group of students in their mock exams.

	Results (%)									
Maths	48	72	56	71	59	70	37	55	59	83
Physics	39	67	51	73	62	65	44	60	59	75

Draw a scatter graph for this data.

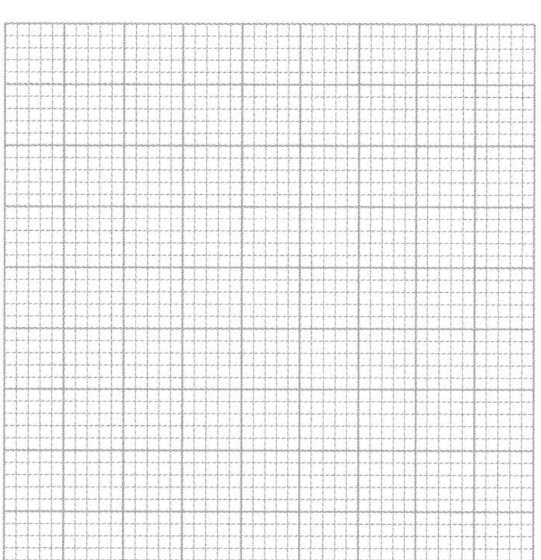

Step into GCSE

3 The results of rolling two dice 15 times are shown in the table.

	Number rolled														
Red dice	3	5	2	2	6	3	4	1	4	3	2	4	6	5	1
Blue dice	4	3	6	4	1	6	4	2	3	3	1	5	2	6	5

Plot the data on a scatter graph.

Needs more practice ☐ Almost there ☐ I'm proficient! ☐

2.9 Misleading diagrams

GCSE LINKS
S: 3.10 Misleading diagrams

By the end of this section you will know how to:

* Recognise misleading diagrams

Key points

Diagrams may be misleading because:

* they have **no scale**
* the scale is **not uniform**
* the scale **does not start from 0**
* the axes are **not labelled**
* lines may be **too thick** to take accurate readings
* **3D effects** may make them difficult to read.

Guided

1 The diagram is intended to indicate that company profits are increasing.

Give two reasons why the diagram is misleading.

1 ....

2 ....

Hint
Think about why it is difficult to take a reading from the graph.

Practice

2 Imagine that the Head of Sales at your company uses this bar chart to show how profits have changed.

Is this a fair representation?
Give a reason for your answer.

....

....

....

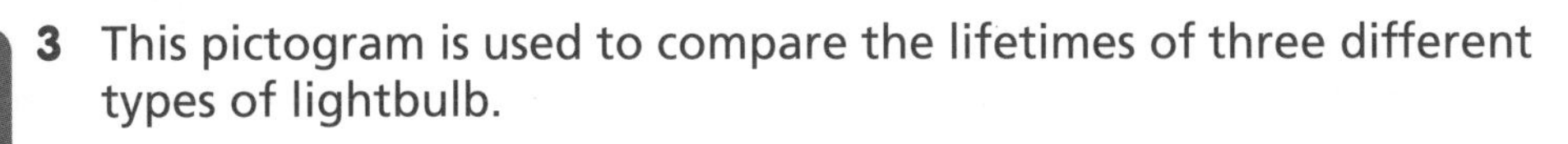

3 This pictogram is used to compare the lifetimes of three different types of lightbulb.

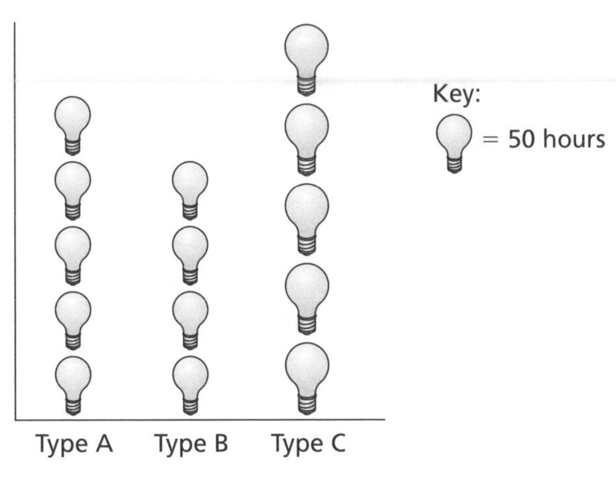

Is the comparison fair? Explain your answer.

....

....

4 Paul wants to show how his football team has improved in the last year. He draws this graph.

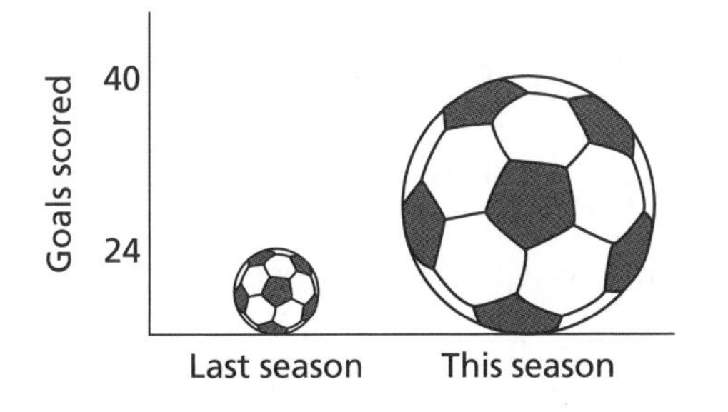

Give two reasons why Paul's graph is misleading.

1 ....

2 ....

5 Suzy has been doing an experiment. She has drawn a graph to show her results.

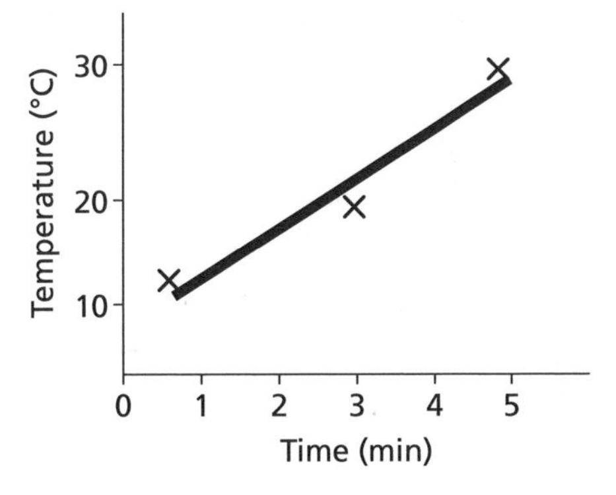

Give two reasons why you think Suzy's graph is misleading.

1 ....

2 ....

6 A company sells brightly coloured novelty T-shirts.
The pie chart shows the proportions of each colour sold.

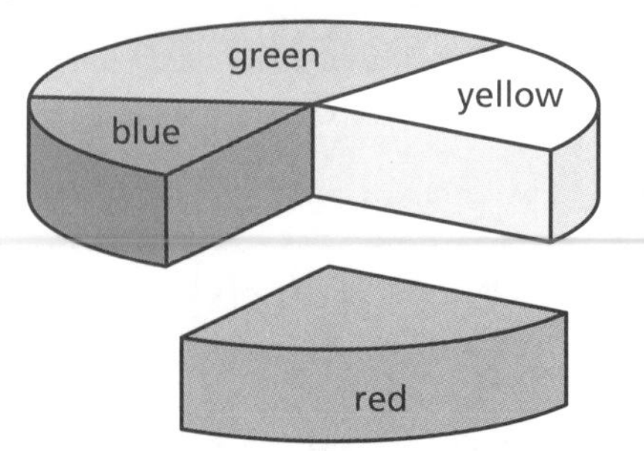

Give two reasons why you think the chart is misleading.

1 ....

2 ....

Don't forget!

* A pictogram should have a .... showing the value of the symbols.
* Bar charts must have a .... between the bars.
* A line graph may be used to display ungrouped .... data.
* A dual bar chart allows .... to be made within a category.
* In a two-way table, the .... of the rows = the total of the ....
* A pie chart is a useful way to compare a .... number of categories.
* In a time-series graph, ... is always shown on the horizontal axis.
* A .... graph is used to show how two variables are related.

Exam-style questions

1 Here is a pictogram showing the numbers of hours of sunshine in Filey during one week.

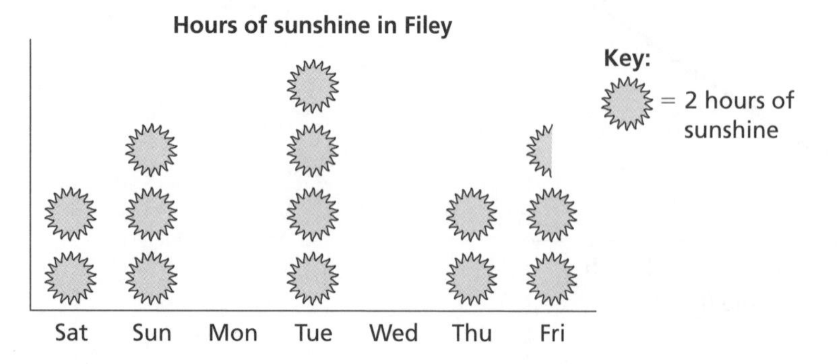

a Complete the pictogram using the information that there were two hours of sunshine on Monday and six hours on Wednesday.

b Draw a bar chart using the grid on the next page to show the same information.

2 The table shows the number of children living in the houses of one street.

Number of children	0	1	2	3	4	5
Frequency	4	6	15	8	3	1

Draw a line graph to show this data.

3 115 people responded to a survey about membership of a new gym.
The results are shown in a two-way table.

	Junior	**Adult**	**Senior**	**Total**
Standard	36	16		57
Full	5	18	10	
Premium		25		
Total	41			

Complete the two-way table.

4 Ade, Baz, Col, Dan and Eve ran two laps of a cross-country course.
The table shows the time in minutes that they each took on each lap.

Name	Ade	Baz	Col	Dan	Eve
Lap 1	38	43	41	37	45
Lap 2	34	52	54	32	45

Draw a dual bar chart to show this data.

5 In a garden, the lawn takes up three times as much space as the bedding plants do.
In the circle, draw a pie chart to represent this information.

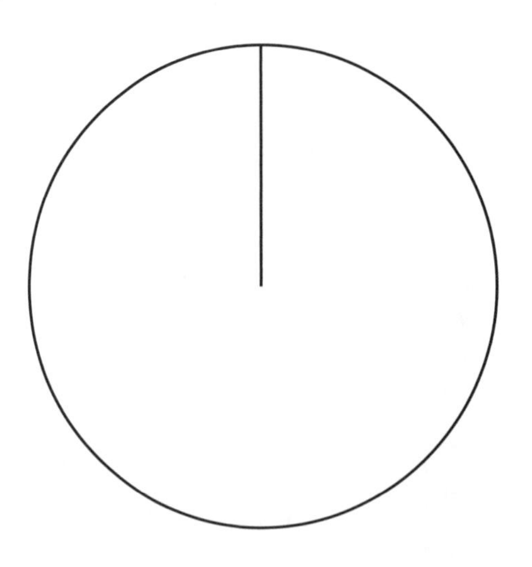

6 Sharon has 45 books. The table shows the categories that they fit into.

Book category	Number of books	Angle of pie chart
Comedy	12	
Thriller	7	
Mystery	9	
Romance	17	

In the circle, draw a pie chart to represent this information.

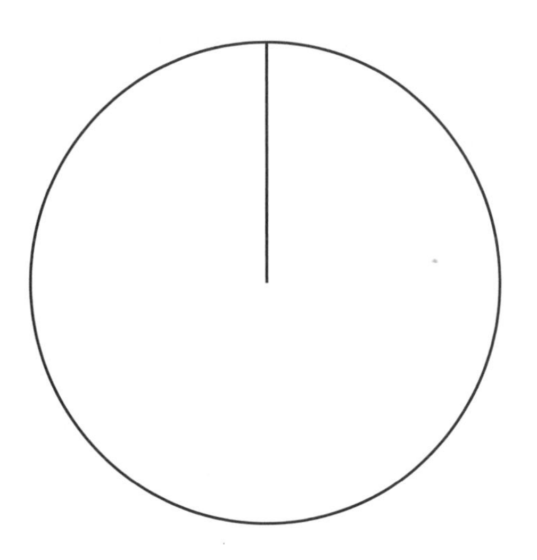

7 The table shows the numbers of houses sold by an estate agent to first-time buyers over a four-year period.

	Year											
	2009			2010			2011			2012		
Period	1	2	3	1	2	3	1	2	3	1	2	3
Houses	28	22	24	9	24	25	26	21	24	34	26	29

Draw a time-series graph to show this information.

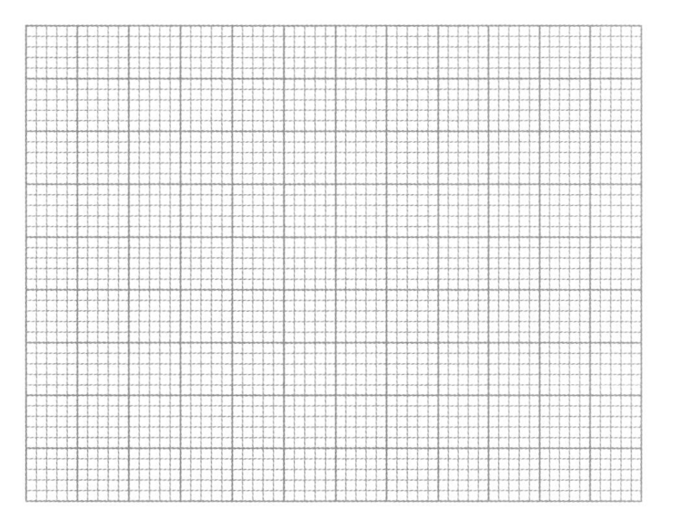

Needs more practice ☐ Almost there ☐ I'm proficient! ☐

3.1 Averages and range

By the end of this section you will know how to:

* Find the mode, median, mean and range of a set of data

GCSE LINKS

AF: 16.1 Mode, median and mean; **BF:** Unit 1 3.2 Mode, median and mean; **16+:** 20.1 Mode, median, mean and range; **S:** 4.2 Mode, median and mean

Key points

* There are three types of average: mode, median and mean.
* The **mode** is the value that occurs **most often** in the data.
* The **median** is the **middle value** once the data is put in order of size.
* If there are two middle values, the median is **halfway** between them.
* The **mean** is found by **adding** all of the data values together and **dividing** by the number of them.
* The **range** measures the **spread** of data. It is the difference between the largest and smallest values in the data.

Guided

1 Helen wanted to know about the colours used for new cars. She looked at ten new cars in a car park and recorded these colours.

white blue white red green
black white red black blue

Find the mode.

Hint The mode is the only average that does not have to be a number.

Hint Which colour appears more than any other in the list?

Mode = ...

2 Paul counts the number of people in each car that passes. Here are his results.

2 1 1 3 2 1
1 2 3 1 2 1

Find the mode of Paul's data.

Hint Look for the number that occurs most often.

Mode = ...

Practice

3 Kath spun a five-sided spinner 10 times. Here are her results.

3 5 4 4 3 1 4 2 5 2

Write down the mode.

Mode = ...

4 Adele counted the number of people at a bus stop at different times of the day. Here are her results.

1 0 3 4 3 2 0 3 5 2 3 1

Write down the mode.

Mode = ...

Step into GCSE

5 The numbers of matches in a sample of ten boxes are shown below.

49 48 46 50 48 47 50 48 49 46

Find the mode.

Mode = ...

6 Lizzy asked ten pupils to name their favourite colour. Here are her results.

green black red blue brown blue red blue black white

Write down the mode.

Mode = ...

Guided

7 Find the median of these nine numbers.

12 18 11 9 16 17 15 16 18

Write the numbers in order: 9 11 12 ....

The median is ....

> **Hint**
> The median is the middle value.

8 Find the median of these eight numbers.

8 9 7 10 7 9 8 10

> **You should know**
> The number of values is even, so there is no middle value.

Write the numbers in order: ....

The numbers in the middle are .... and ....

The median is ....

> **Hint**
> The median is halfway between the pair of numbers in the middle.

Practice

9 Here are the heights of the members of the Year 11 football team in centimetres.

183 176 175 180 182 180 181 172 178 185 179

Find the median height.

Median height = ... cm

10 Ten children were asked how many Easter eggs they had received. Here are the results.

11 7 6 7 10 9 6 9 7 12

Find the median.

Median number of eggs = ...

GCSE

11 Eight Year 11 boys tried to do as many press-ups as possible in one attempt.
Here are the results.

23 16 14 28 11 36 57 19

Find the median.

Median number of press-ups = ...

12 The cooking times in minutes of ten frozen ready meals are shown below.

11 16 18 12 17 20 15 10 15 16

Find the median.

Median cooking time = ... minutes

Guided

13 Work out the mean of these eight football scores.

3 0 2 1 5 2 1 2

Total = 3 + 0 + 2 + ... = ...

Mean = ... ÷ .... = ...

Hint

Divide the total by the number of scores.

14 Jackie went ten-pin bowling. Her first six attempts produced these scores.

3 5 1 7 4 10

Calculate Jackie's mean score.

Total = ...

Mean = ... ÷ .... = ...

Practice

15 Here are the numbers of letters that Tom received during a six-day period.

4 3 6 5 4 8

Calculate the mean number of letters Tom received each day.

Mean = ...

16 Leslie made nine bunches of flowers.
Here are the numbers of flowers she used in the bunches.

10 12 11 15 13 16 12 8 11

Work out the mean number of flowers per bunch.

Mean = ...

Step into GCSE

17 Eight swimmers took part in a sponsored swim.
The numbers of lengths they completed are shown below.

21 16 25 30 34 18 22 26

Calculate the mean number of lengths each person swam.

Mean = ...

18 Here are the numbers of people staying in ten caravans.

4 3 2 5 4 4 3 2 6 3

Work out the mean number of people per caravan.

Mean = ...

Guided

19 The monthly salaries of eight employees are shown below.

£965 £824 £1026 £872 £1105 £988 £1009 £978

Work out the range.

Largest salary = ... Smallest salary = ...

Range = ... − .... = ...

Remember this

The range is the difference between the largest salary and the smallest salary.

Practice

20 Five friends each threw one dart at a dart board. Their scores are shown below.

19 1 20 60 18

Work out the range.

Range = ...

21 Seven pupils gave these estimates of the height of a building in metres.

10 7 8.6 10.5 9 9.4 8

Work out the range.

Range = ...

GCSE

22 Six members of a running club ran a half marathon. Here are their times.

1 h 26 min 1h 15 min 2h 11 min 1h 45 min 1h 52 min 1h 38 min

Work out the range.

Range = ...

23 In a strongman contest, competitors had to hurl barrels over a steel wall. The times taken were:

1 min 18 sec 1 min 12 sec 23 sec 1 min 17 sec 21sec 1 min 11 sec

Work out the range.

Range = ...

24 The lowest overnight temperatures in eight UK cities in January were:

−2°C 0°C −4°C −7°C −3°C −8°C −6°C −12°C

Work out the range.

Range = ...

Needs more practice ☐ Almost there ☐ I'm proficient! ☐

Range and mode from a stem and leaf diagram

GCSE LINKS
AF: 16.4 Stem and leaf diagrams; **BF:** Unit 1 3.6 Stem and leaf diagrams; **16+:** 20.2 Stem and leaf diagrams; **S:** 3.2 Stem and leaf diagrams

By the end of this section you will know how to:

* Find the range and mode from a stem and leaf diagram

Key points

* The stem and leaf diagram should be **ordered** first.
* The **smallest** number is given by the **first** leaf.
* The **largest** number is given by the **last** leaf.
* The number repeated **most often** in a row indicates the **mode**.

Guided

1 Here is an unordered stem and leaf diagram.

1	6	2	1	5	
2	7	8	3	7	2
3	6	4	1		
4	2	9	0	3	

Key: 2|3 means 23

Show this information in an ordered stem and leaf diagram.

1	1	2	....
2	2	3	....
3	1	4	....
4	0	2	....

Key: 2|3 means 23

You should know
The numbers in each row need to be put in order, smallest on the left.

Hint
Keep the numbers in tidy columns equally spaced.

2 Use your ordered stem and leaf diagram from Question 1 to find the mode.

You should know
Look for the value repeated most often in a row.

Hint
When you write down the mode, use the key and remember to include the stem.

Mode = ...

3 Here is an ordered stem and leaf diagram. Find the range.

3	(4)	4	5	7		
4	2	4	5	6	8	
5	0	1	1	4	7	9
6	0	7	9			
7	1	6	7	(8)		

Key: 5|4 means 54

Hint
The first leaf and the last leaf are circled.
Remember to use the key.

Largest number = ... Smallest number = ...

Range = ...

Practice

4 Claire checked the pulse rates of 20 people at a gym.
She showed her results in an ordered stem and leaf diagram.

5	8	9								
6	0	2	3	3	3	5	5	5	7	9
7	2	3	3	4	6					
8	1	2								
9	0									

Key: 7 | 3 means 73 beats per minute

a Find the mode of the pulse rates.

Mode = ... beats per minute

b Find the range of the pulse rates.

Range = ... beats per minute

5 Shaun asked some students how many digital albums they had.
The ordered stem and leaf diagram shows his results.

2	6	7	9				
3	2	5	7	8	9		
4	1	4	5	6	6	8	
5	1	3	3	3	7	7	9
6	2	3	4	4	8		
7	2	3					

Key: 4 | 6 means 46 albums

a Work out the range.

Range = ...

b Find the mode.

Mode = ...

6 Lily measured the speeds of cars along a main road in miles per hour. She recorded her results as an unordered stem and leaf diagram.

2	9	9						
3	7	0	1	4	8	7		
4	8	9	3	5	4	8	6	9
5	0	7	3	7	4	7	8	
6	6	4	3					

Key: 4 | 3 means 43 miles per hour

a Show the information in an ordered stem and leaf diagram.

b Find the mode of the speeds.

Mode = ... miles per hour

c Find the range of the speeds.

Range = ... miles per hour

7 The amounts of tax paid in one month by 20 employees of a company are shown in the stem and leaf diagram. Each amount has been rounded to the nearest £10.

2	2	6	8					
3	1	5	5	7	8			
4	2	2	2	3	6	7	7	8
5	3	8	9	9				

Key: 3 | 7 means £370

a Find the mode of the amount of tax paid.

Mode = ...

b Work out the range of the amount of tax paid.

Range = ...

Don't forget!

* The mode, median and mean are three types of ....
* The mode is the value that occurs ....
* To find the median, first put the values in ....
* To find the mean, divide the .... by the ....
* The .... measures the spread of the data.
* The smallest value in an .... stem and leaf diagram is given by the first leaf.
* The number repeated most often in the rows of a stem and leaf diagram tells us what to combine with the stem to find the value of the ....

Exam-style questions

1 Eleven adults were asked how many close friends they had. Here are the results.

1 3 1 2 4 2 1 3 1 2 5

a Find the mode.

Mode = ...

b Find the median.

Median = ...

c Work out the mean.

Mean = ...

2 In a gym test, the 11 members of a football team did as many sit-ups as they could in one minute. Here are the results.

48 72 55 64 58 52 49 56 70 64 61

a Work out the mean.

Mean = ...

b Find the median.

Median = ...

c Work out the range.

Range = ...

3 Bill recorded the times taken (in seconds) by a sample of ten cars to travel along a stretch of motorway. Here are his results.

26 23 22 19 23 21 23 22 25 26

a Find the mode.

Mode = ... seconds

b Find the median.

Median = ... seconds

c Work out the mean.

Mean = ... seconds

4 The stem and leaf diagram shows the numbers of rainy days in one year for 23 American cities.

12	3	6	6				
13	2	4	4	5	5	7	
14	3	5	7	8	8		
15	4	7	8	8	8	9	9
16	4	5					

Key: 14 | 7 represents 147 rainy days

a Find the mode of the number of rainy days.

Mode = ... days

b Find the range of the number of rainy days.

Range = ... days

5 Sophia asked 20 runners in the London Marathon how many miles they ran in the week before the event. Her results are shown in the stem and leaf diagram.

1	0	2	5	8	8	
2	2	5	6			
3	0	1	4	4	4	6
4	2	6	6	8		
5	2	2				

Key: 2 | 5 represents 25 miles

a Find the mode of miles run.

Mode = ... miles

b Work out the range.

Range = ... miles

4.1 Read and interpret data presented in tables

GCSE LINKS
AF: 3.5 Two-way and other tables; **BF:** Unit 1 5.7 Two-way tables; **S:** 2.5 Two-way tables

By the end of this section you will know how to:

* Find and understand information given in tables

Key points

* Use the labels on the rows and columns to find information.
* You may need to add values in a row or column to find a total.
* You may need to subtract one value from another in the table to find a difference.

Guided

1 The table shows the number of students in each year group in a secondary school.

Year group	Number of students
11	124
10	116
9	137
8	128
7	112

a How many students are in Year 11? ....

b Which is the largest year group? ....

Hint
Look for the largest number in the second column. Find the matching year group.

c The senior students are in Years 10 and 11.
How many senior students are there?

Hint
Add the number of students in Year 10 to the number of students in Year 11.

....

2 Here is part of a train timetable. It shows the time that a train leaves each station.

Station	Time
Bempton	1253
Hunmanby	1303
Filey	1308
Seamer	1320
Scarborough	1325

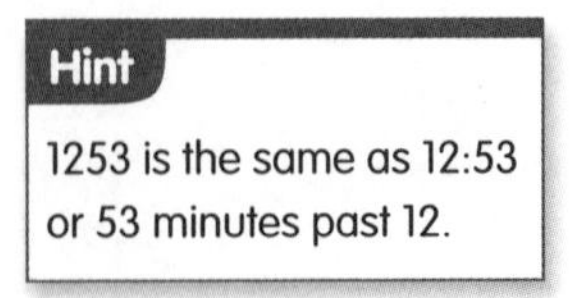

a What time does the train leave Hunmanby? ....

b The train is in Seamer station for 3 minutes. What time did the train arrive at Seamer?

Hint
Work out the time that is 3 minutes earlier than the time shown for Seamer.

....

3 The table shows the numbers of people attending a cinema on one day.
There are four screens, each showing a different film.
Each film is shown twice on the same screen.

	First show	Second show
Screen 1	462	578
Screen 2	389	547
Screen 3	536	672
Screen 4	496	758

Hint
Find the number in the row for Screen 2 and the column for the second show.

a How many people saw the second show on Screen 2? ....

b How many people attended the first show?

Hint
There are four numbers to add for the first show.

....

c How many people saw the most popular film?

Hint
Find the largest total for the first and second shows.

....

4 The table shows the distances in miles between some cities in England.

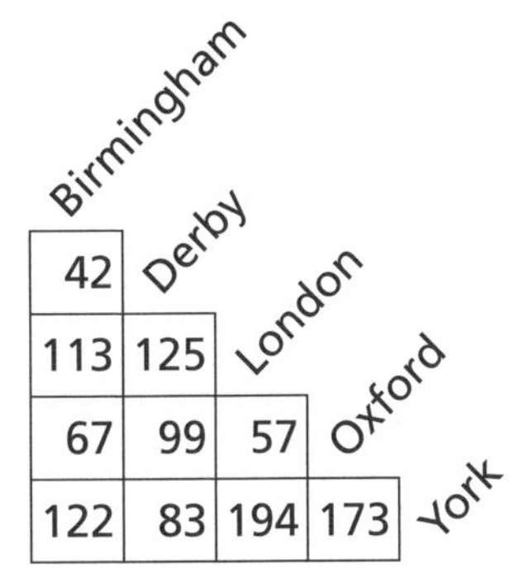

Birmingham				
42	Derby			
113	125	London		
67	99	57	Oxford	
122	83	194	173	York

a Find the distance from Birmingham to London.

Hint
Follow the column down from Birmingham until it meets the row across from London.

.... miles

b Which city is 83 miles from Derby?

Hint
Look for 83 in the same row or column as Derby.
Find the other city in the same row or column as 83.

....

c Sharon drives from York to Birmingham and then from Birmingham to London.
How far does Sharon drive altogether?

Hint
Find the two distances and add them.

.... miles

Practice

5 The table shows the midday temperatures in five towns.

Location	Temperature
Cardiff	$-3°C$
Lancaster	$-1°C$
Poole	$2°C$
Stone	$1°C$
Whitby	$-2°C$

a What is the temperature in Whitby? ....

b Which is the coldest location? ....

c How much warmer is Poole than Whitby? ....

6 Here is part of a train timetable. It shows the time that the train leaves each station.

Station	Time
Thirsk	0610
Northallerton	0618
Darlington	0636
Thornaby	0653
Middlesbrough	0703

a What time does the train leave Thornaby? ....

b The train stops at Middlesbrough for 5 minutes. How long does it take to get from Darlington to Middlesbrough?

.... minutes

7 The table shows the numbers of cars sold by five sales people over a four-week period.

	Week 1	Week 2	Week 3	Week 4
Graham	3	4	3	4
Jinty	4	3	4	6
Matt	4	2	4	4
Sally	3	3	4	5
Mike	2	3	4	4

a How many cars did Mike sell in Week 2? ....

b How many cars were sold altogether in Week 1? ....

c Who sold the most cars? ....

d How many more cars were sold in Week 4 than in Week 3? ....

8 The table shows the distances in miles between some English cities.

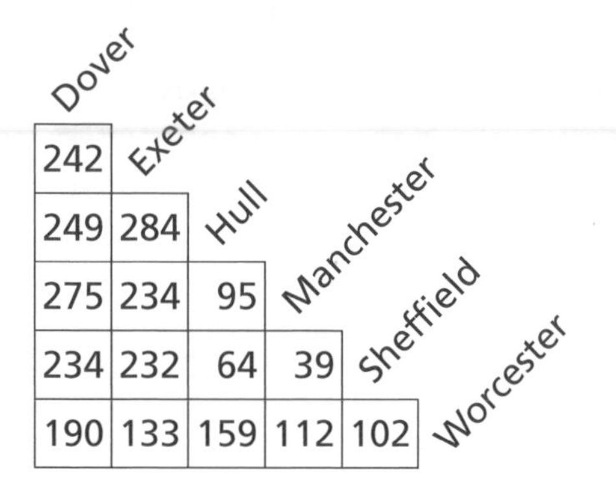

	Dover	Exeter	Hull	Manchester	Sheffield
Exeter	242				
Hull	249	284			
Manchester	275	234	95		
Sheffield	234	232	64	39	
Worcester	190	133	159	112	102

a How far is it from Hull to Sheffield? .... miles

b Which city is less than 200 miles from Dover? ....

c Which city is closest to Hull? ....

d Kari drives from Dover to Sheffield and then from Sheffield to Hull.
How far does she drive altogether?

.... miles

e Kari returns to Dover without going to Sheffield. How much shorter is this route?

.... miles

GCSE

9 Records of rainfall in the UK go back to 1910.
The table shows the amounts of rainfall for the wettest five years in that time.

Year	Rainfall (mm)
1954	1309
2000	1337
2002	1284
2008	1295
2012	1331

a How many of the five wettest years have occurred from 2000 onwards? ....

b Which year was the wettest? ....

c How many years are there between the two most recent entries in the table?

....

d How many years are there between the two oldest entries in the table?

....

10 Jasmine owns an ice cream parlour. The table shows how many litres of her top-selling flavours she sold each month between June and August.

	June	July	August
Belgian chocolate	126	142	135
Chocolate mint chip	94	110	102
Raspberry ripple	88	116	79
Rum and raisin	143	182	156
Vanilla	107	123	112

a Which flavour is the most popular? ....

b How much Belgian chocolate flavour ice cream was sold in July? .... litres

c In which month was the most ice cream sold? ....

d How much in total of all of these flavours was sold in June?

.... litres

e How much more Rum and raisin was sold than Vanilla over the three months?

.... litres

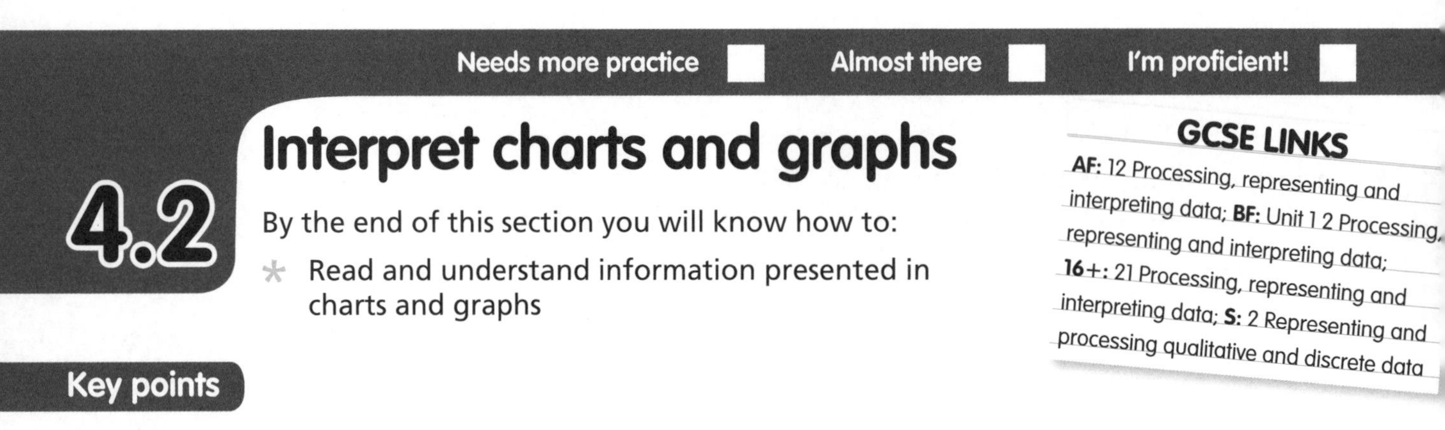

Needs more practice ☐ Almost there ☐ I'm proficient! ☐

4.2 Interpret charts and graphs

By the end of this section you will know how to:

* Read and understand information presented in charts and graphs

GCSE LINKS

AF: 12 Processing, representing and interpreting data; **BF:** Unit 1 2 Processing, representing and interpreting data; **16+:** 21 Processing, representing and interpreting data; **S:** 2 Representing and processing qualitative and discrete data

Key points

* Use the title or description of the diagram to find out what it is about.
* Look at the labels and try to compare values or look for a pattern.

Pictograms

Guided

1 The pictogram shows the number of cars cleaned at a car wash each day for one week.

Monday	
Tuesday	
Wednesday	
Thursday	
Friday	
Saturday	

Key: 🚗 = 10 cars

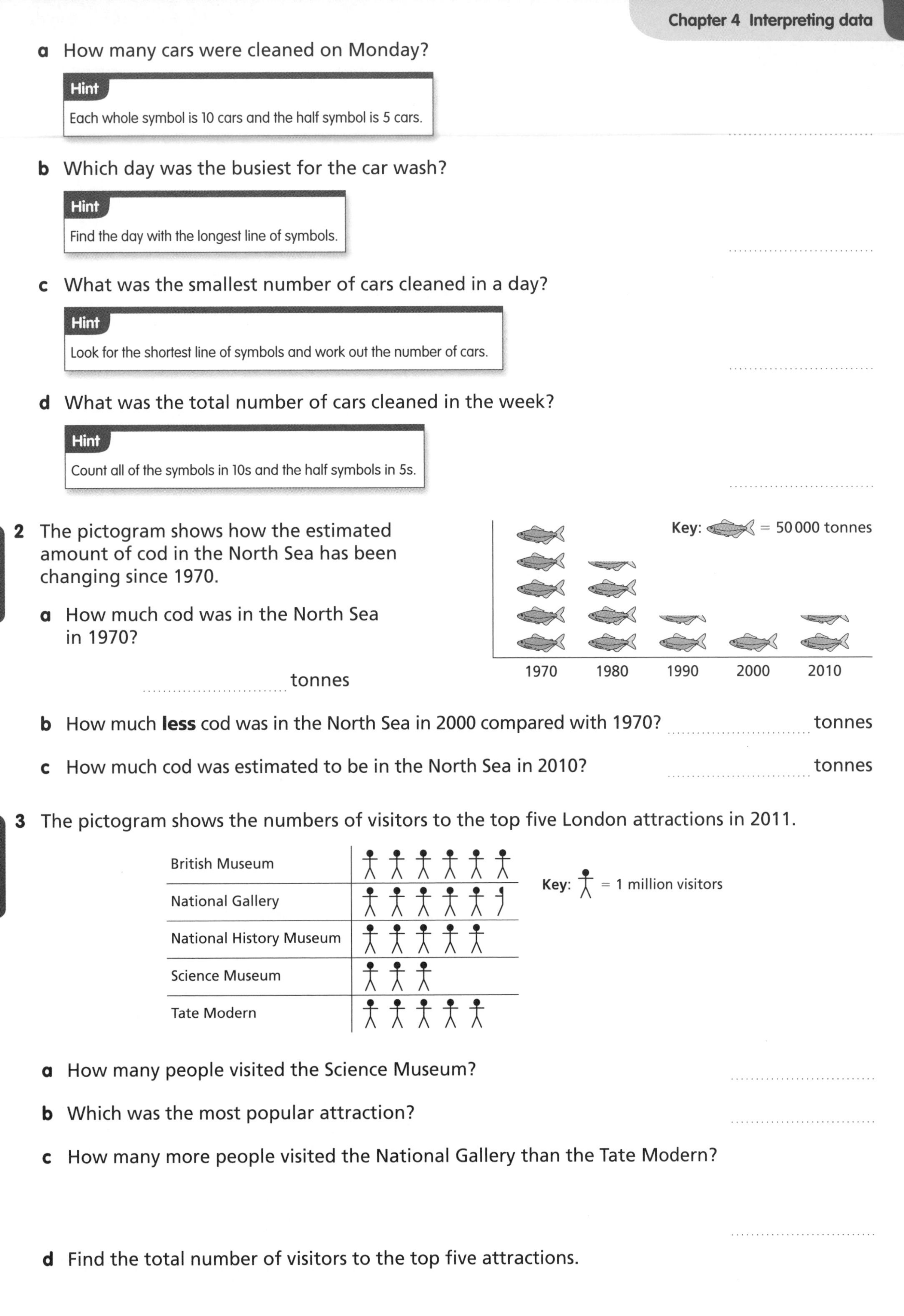

a How many cars were cleaned on Monday?

> **Hint**
> Each whole symbol is 10 cars and the half symbol is 5 cars.

....

b Which day was the busiest for the car wash?

> **Hint**
> Find the day with the longest line of symbols.

....

c What was the smallest number of cars cleaned in a day?

> **Hint**
> Look for the shortest line of symbols and work out the number of cars.

....

d What was the total number of cars cleaned in the week?

> **Hint**
> Count all of the symbols in 10s and the half symbols in 5s.

....

Practice

2 The pictogram shows how the estimated amount of cod in the North Sea has been changing since 1970.

a How much cod was in the North Sea in 1970?

.... tonnes

b How much **less** cod was in the North Sea in 2000 compared with 1970? .... tonnes

c How much cod was estimated to be in the North Sea in 2010? .... tonnes

GCSE

3 The pictogram shows the numbers of visitors to the top five London attractions in 2011.

a How many people visited the Science Museum? ....

b Which was the most popular attraction? ....

c How many more people visited the National Gallery than the Tate Modern?

....

d Find the total number of visitors to the top five attractions.

....

Bar charts

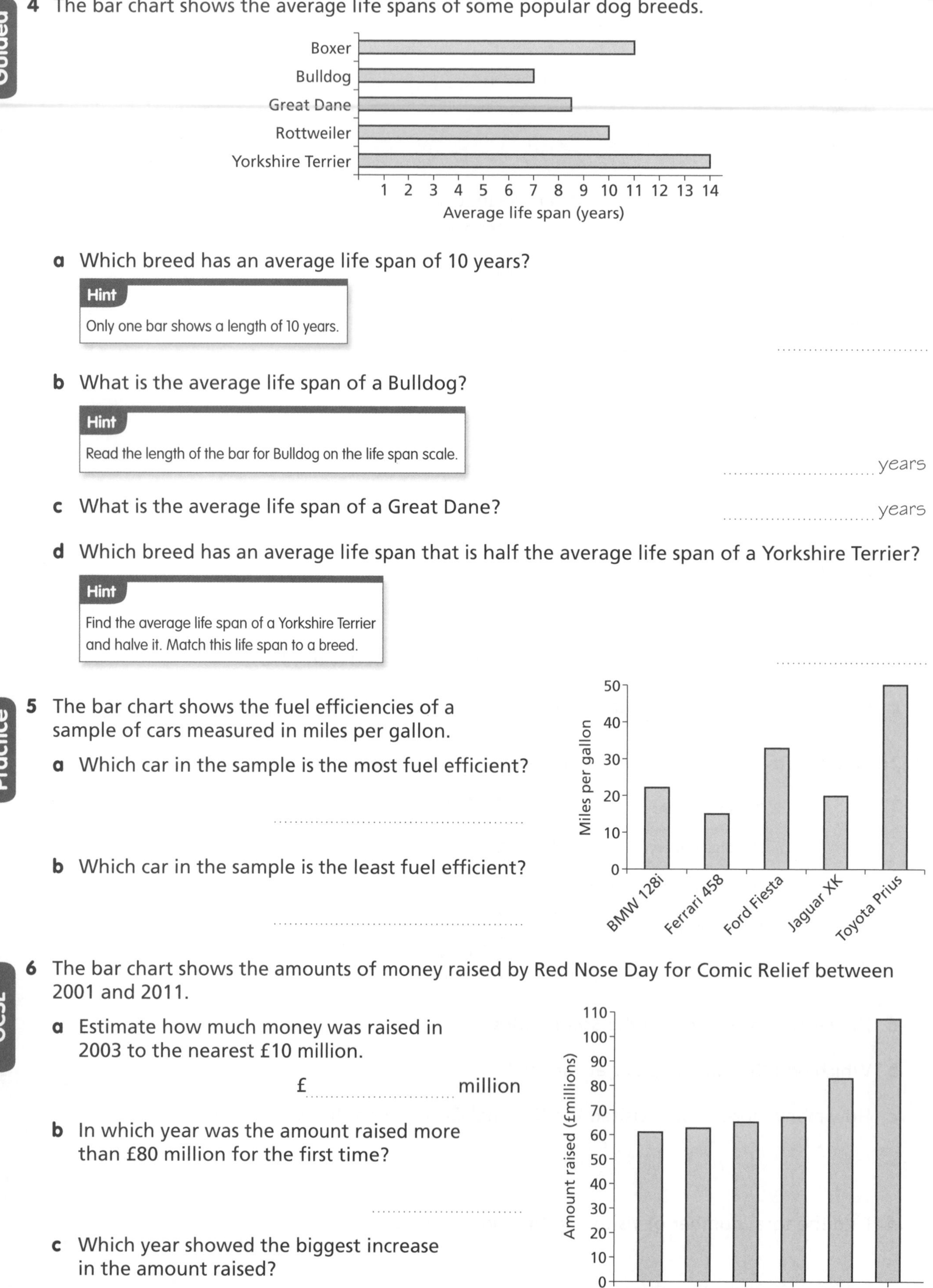

Guided

4 The bar chart shows the average life spans of some popular dog breeds.

a Which breed has an average life span of 10 years?

> **Hint**
> Only one bar shows a length of 10 years.

....

b What is the average life span of a Bulldog?

> **Hint**
> Read the length of the bar for Bulldog on the life span scale.

.... years

c What is the average life span of a Great Dane? .... years

d Which breed has an average life span that is half the average life span of a Yorkshire Terrier?

> **Hint**
> Find the average life span of a Yorkshire Terrier and halve it. Match this life span to a breed.

....

Practice

5 The bar chart shows the fuel efficiencies of a sample of cars measured in miles per gallon.

a Which car in the sample is the most fuel efficient?

....

b Which car in the sample is the least fuel efficient?

....

Step into GCSE

6 The bar chart shows the amounts of money raised by Red Nose Day for Comic Relief between 2001 and 2011.

a Estimate how much money was raised in 2003 to the nearest £10 million.

£.............................. million

b In which year was the amount raised more than £80 million for the first time?

....

c Which year showed the biggest increase in the amount raised?

....

Line graphs

7 Some Year 9 students were selected at random and given a test to check their attainment levels in maths. The line graph shows the results.

a How many students are at level 8? ....

Hint

Read off the height of the point for level 8.

b Which level is the mode? ....

Remember this

The mode is the value that occurs most often.

c How many students are at level 6 or higher? ....

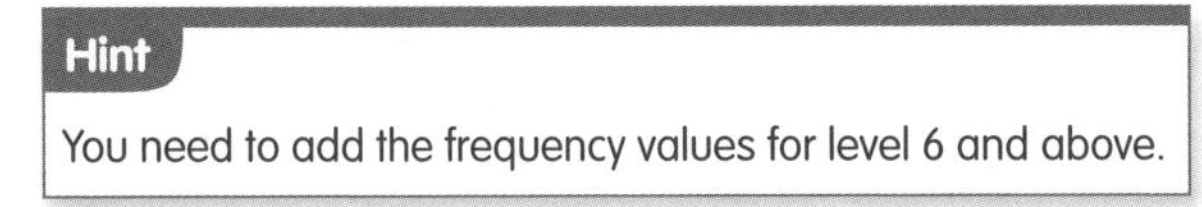

Hint

You need to add the frequency values for level 6 and above.

d How many Year 9 students were selected? ....

Hint

You need to add the frequency values for all of the levels.

Practice

8 A primary school teacher asked each member of her class to choose a number from 2 to 8. The line graph below on the left shows the results.

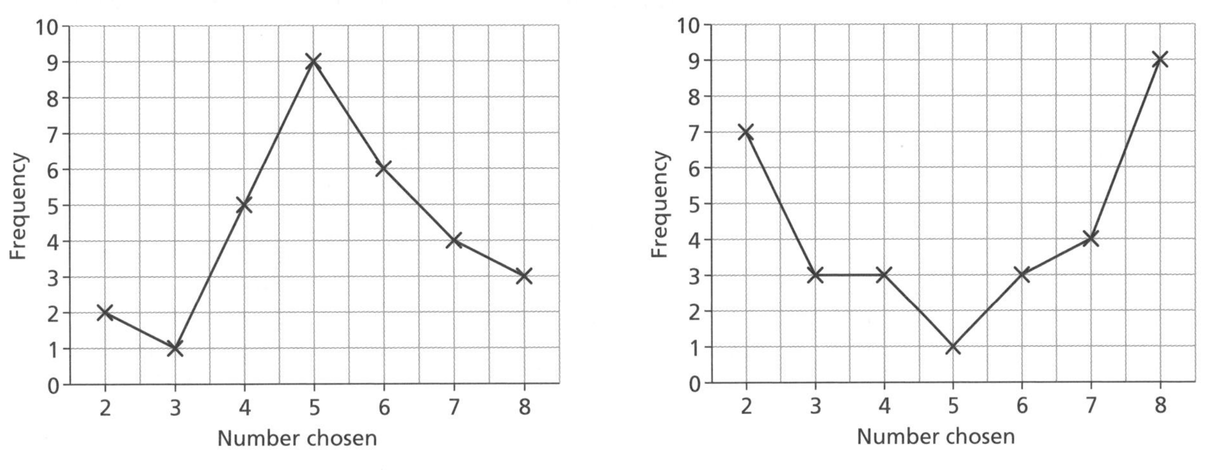

The teacher then explained that people often choose numbers towards the middle of the range and avoid numbers at the ends. She then asked the class to choose a number again. The line graph above on the right shows the second set of results.

a Which number was the mode the first time? ....

b Which number was the mode the second time? ....

c Which number was chosen with the same frequency both times? ....

d How many children are in the class?

....

e Describe the change in the results.

....

....

....

Step into GCSE

9 Charlotte recorded the number of customers in her seaside café between 0900 and 1500 one day. The line graph shows this information.

a What is the lowest number of customers shown on the graph?

....

b Explain how there may have been times between 0900 and 1500 when the number of customers was lower than this.

....

....

....

....

Dual bar charts

Guided

10 The dual bar chart shows how the estimated populations of red squirrels and grey squirrels in the UK have been changing since 1965.

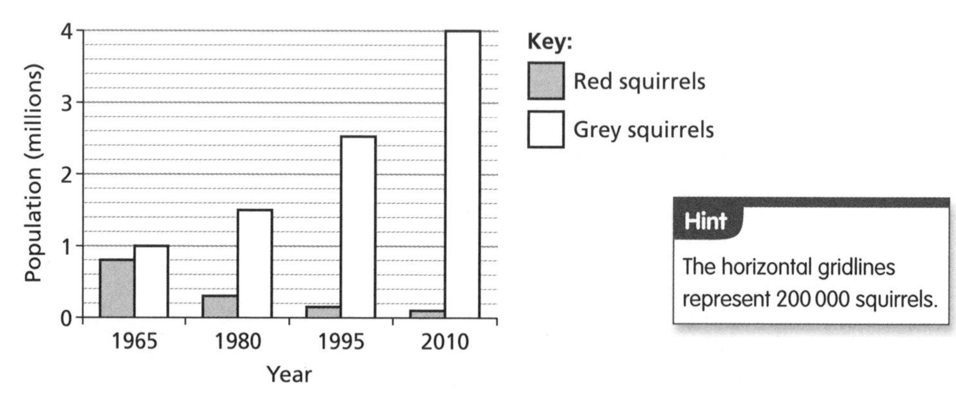

a What was the estimated population of red squirrels in 1965? *800 000*

b What was the estimated population of red squirrels in 1980? ....

c When was the population of grey squirrels roughly five times the population of red squirrels?

> **Hint**
> Find the year in which this looks most likely and then work out the populations.

....

d Roughly how many grey squirrels were there for every red squirrel in 2010?

> **Hint**
> Start by working out the populations of red and grey squirrels in 2010.

....

Practice

11 The dual bar chart shows how the average prices of diesel and unleaded petrol have been changing since 2008.

a Overall, which has been the more expensive fuel since 2008? ....

b In which years did diesel and petrol cost the same? .... and ....

c In which year was the difference in price greatest? ....

GCSE

12 The dual bar chart shows the numbers of boy and girl babies born at a maternity ward each week over a five-week period.

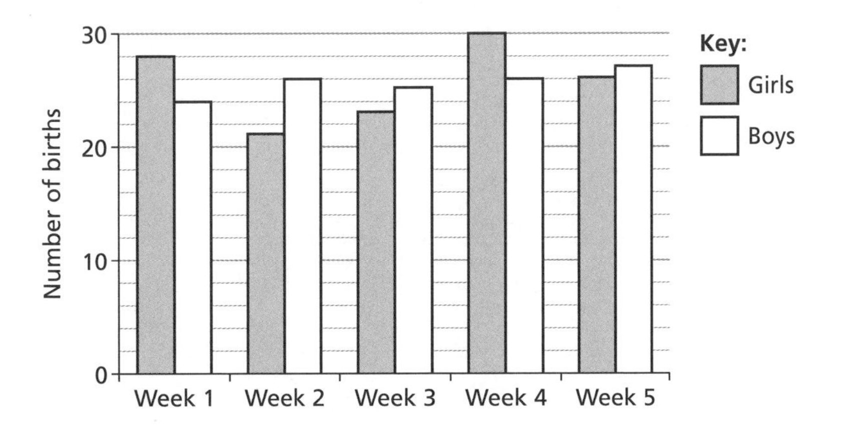

a How many girls were born in Week 3? ....

b How many more boys than girls were born in Week 2? ....

c In how many of the five weeks were more girls born than boys? ....

d In which week were the most girls born? ....

e What is the range of the total number of births in a week?

....

Pie charts

Guided

13 Kelly did a survey among young adults to find out what they would most like to learn in the near future.
The pie chart shows her results.

a What was the most popular response?

> **Hint**
> Look for the sector with the largest angle.

....

b Which response was just as popular as 'Learn to dance'?

> **Hint**
> Look for the sector with the same angle as 'Learn to dance'.

....

c Nine people chose 'Learn a language'.
How many people took the survey?

60° represents 9 people and 360° = 6 × 60°

so total number of people = 9 × .... = ...

Practice

14 A mobile phone company asked 84 customers to choose the most unexpected use of a mobile phone from a list of five possibilities. The pie chart shows the results.

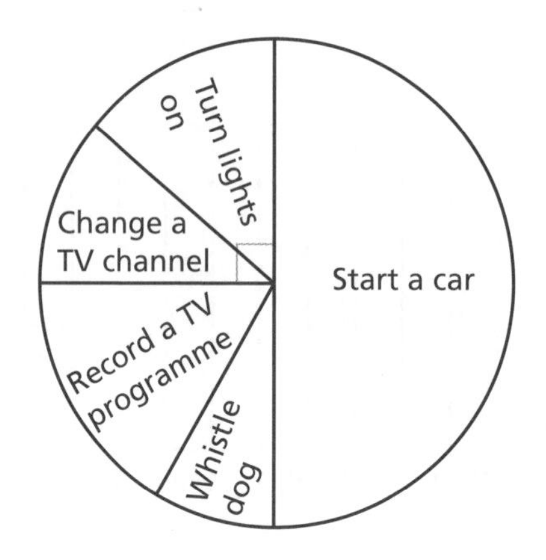

a How many customers chose 'Start a car'?

....

b How many customers chose either 'Turn lights on' or 'Change a TV channel'?

....

c Twice as many customers chose 'Record a TV programme' as 'Whistle dog'.
How many chose 'Whistle dog'?

....

GCSE

15 The pie chart shows how Karen spends her wages.
Karen earns £270 per week.

Savings
Household bills
120°
Entertainment
60°
40°
Clothes & make-up
Transport

a How much does she spend on household bills?

....

b She saves as much as she spends on entertainment.
How much does she save each week?

....

c She spends twice as much on transport as she does on clothes and make-up.
How much does she spend on transport?

....

Time-series graphs

Guided

16 The time-series graph shows the number of umbrellas sold by a shop each month in one year.

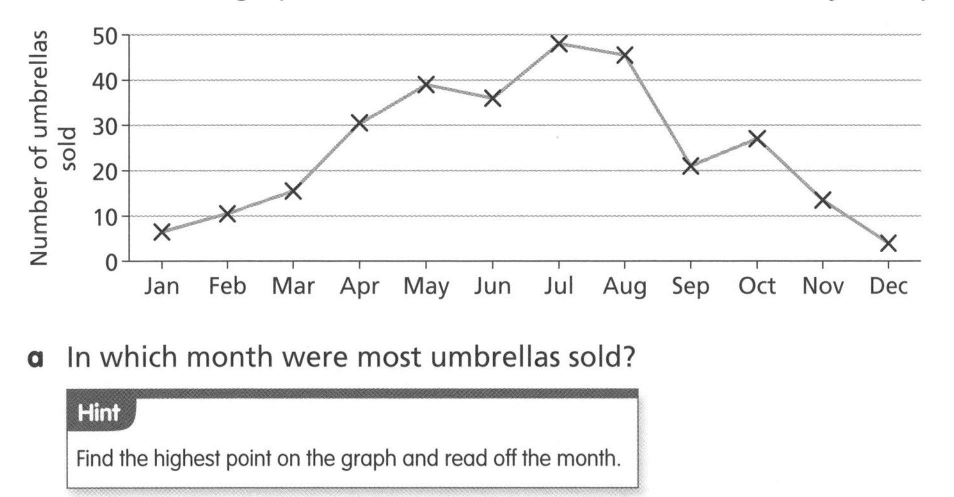

a In which month were most umbrellas sold?

Hint
Find the highest point on the graph and read off the month.

....

b In which month were fewest umbrellas sold? ....

c In which month were twice as many umbrellas sold as in March?

Hint
Find the number sold in March and double it.
Look for the month when this many were sold.

....

d How many umbrellas were sold in February? ....

e Do you think that the shop is in the UK? Give a reason for your answer.

....

....

....

17 The time-series graph shows how the temperature at a resort varied throughout the day.

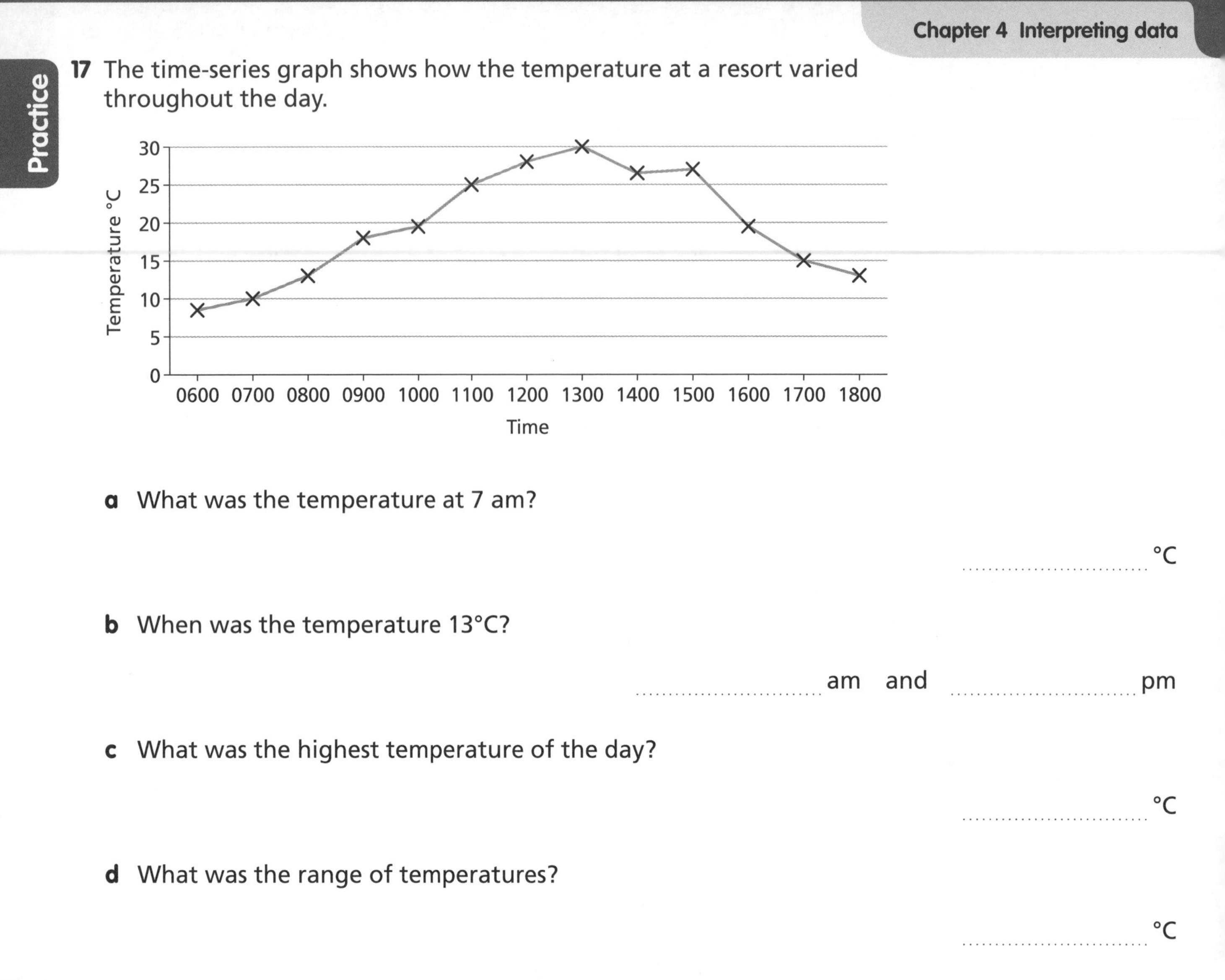

a What was the temperature at 7 am?

.... °C

b When was the temperature 13°C?

.... am and .... pm

c What was the highest temperature of the day?

.... °C

d What was the range of temperatures?

.... °C

18 The time-series graph shows the number of barbecue units sold each quarter over a three-year period.

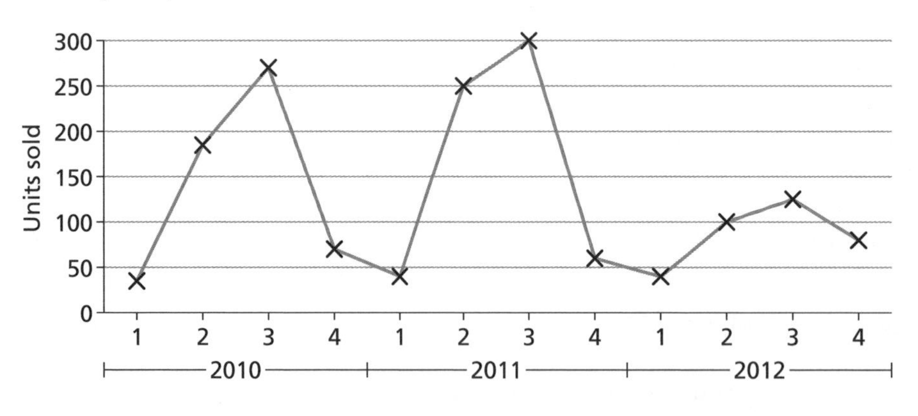

a One of these years was the second wettest on record.
Which was it?

....

b In which quarter were sales the highest each year?

....

c How many units were sold in the second quarter of 2011?

....

Scatter graphs

19 The scatter graph shows the scores on Paper 1 and Paper 2 of a maths test for a group of students.

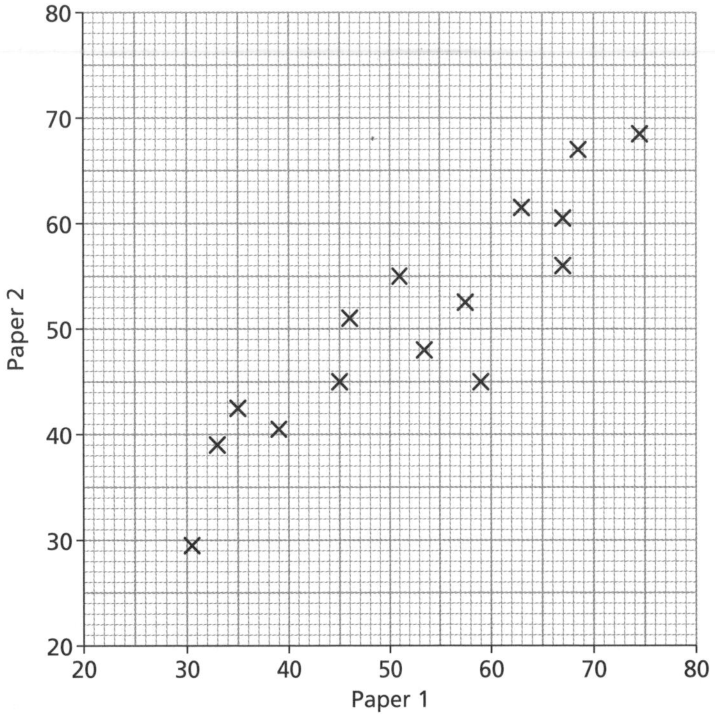

a One student scored the same on both papers. What was that score?

> **Hint**
> Equal scores are found on the diagonal from the bottom corner.

....

b Another student scored 51 marks on Paper 1. What was their mark on Paper 2?

> **Hint**
> There is only one cross showing a mark of 51 on Paper 1. Read off the Paper 2 score.

....

Practice

20 A group of students ranked their own revision books by awarding each one a number of stars from 0 to 5. They also recorded the number of pages for each book. The scatter graph shows this information.

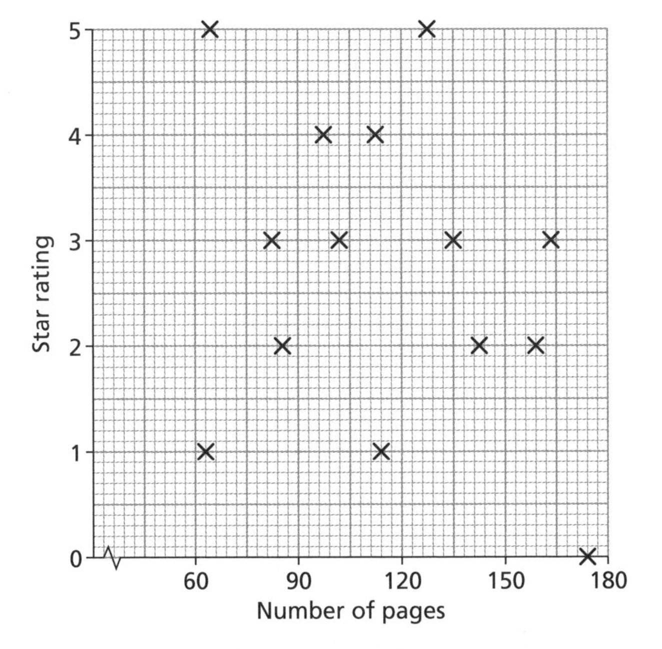

a How many books had a star rating of 3? ....

b How many books had more than 150 pages? ....

c A book of 120 pages was given a star rating of 4. Show this information on the graph.

d What was the modal rating given to the revision books?

....

> **Remember this**
> The mode, or modal value, is the value that occurs most often in the data.

Step into GCSE

21 Mike has been studying the movement of vehicles approaching traffic lights. He noticed that when the lights change to green, each vehicle in the queue is delayed an amount of time before it can move. The scatter graph shows his results.

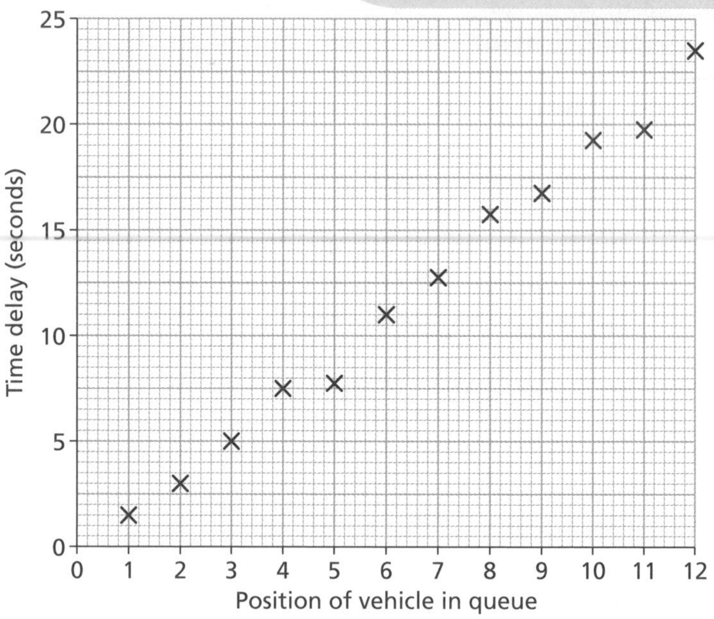

a How long was the delay for the fifth vehicle in the queue?

.... seconds

b How many vehicles had started to move within 20 seconds?

....

Needs more practice ☐ Almost there ☐ I'm proficient! ☐

4.3 Find totals and modes from frequency tables or diagrams

GCSE LINKS

AF: 16.1 Mode, median and mean; **BF:** Unit 1 3.2 Mode, median and mean; **16+:** 20.3 Using frequency tables to find averages; **S:** 4.3 Mode, median and mean in a frequency table

By the end of this section you will know how to:

* Calculate totals and find the mode of data from a frequency table or diagram

Key points

* You may need to add an extra row or column to a frequency table to find the total.
* The mode is the value that occurs with the highest frequency.

Guided

1 The table shows the total numbers of goals scored in some hockey matches.

Goals scored	1	2	3	4	5
Frequency	5	8	6	4	2

Hint
You need the total of the frequency values.

a How many matches were played? ....

b How many goals were scored altogether?

Goals scored (G)	Frequency (F)	G × F
1	5	5
2	8	16
3	6	
4	4	
5	2	
Totals		

Hint
You need to multiply each number of goals by its frequency. Add the answers.

Hint
Adding is easier in columns so it is helpful to redraw the table with an extra column.

Total number of goals scored = ...

2 Gary collected a sample of strawberry punnets of the same size.
He counted the number of strawberries in each one.
The table shows his results.

Number of strawberries (S)	Frequency (F)	S × .....
10	1	10
11	3	33
12	11	
13	9	
14	4	
15	2	
Totals		

a Work out the number of punnets in Gary's sample. ....

b Work out the total numbers of strawberries in all the punnets. ....

3 The table shows the numbers of people travelling per car during a survey.

Number of people (P)	Frequency (F)	
1	32	
2	21	
3	12	
4	8	
5	3	

a How many cars were observed in the survey? ....

b Find the total number of people in the cars. ....

4 The table shows the number of students in each classroom of a school during period 1 on a Monday.

Number of students	12	16	28	29	30	31	32
Frequency	3	2	7	11	14	12	9

a How many classrooms were observed? ....

b Work out the total number of students in all the classrooms.

....

Guided

5 Sonia asked the students in her group to write down the names of as many Harry Potter films as they could. The table shows her results.

Number of films	1	2	3	4	5	6	7	8
Frequency	3	5	7	4	3	4	1	2

Hint

The mode is the value that occurs with the highest frequency.

What is the mode of the number of films named? ....

Practice

6 Stephen is interested in styles of music. He carried out a survey to find out what people like. The table shows his results.

Music style	Blues	Country	Hip hop	Jazz	Pop	Rock
Frequency	11	9	16	12	24	18

Which style is the mode? ....

Step into GCSE

7 Gavin organises a cracker eating contest.
The object is to eat as many crackers as possible within one minute.
No drinks are allowed.
The results are shown in the table.

Number of crackers	**Frequency**
1	4
2	8
3	5
4	2
5	1

a How many people took part in the contest?

....

b How many crackers were eaten in total?

....

c What is the mode for the number of crackers eaten?

....

8 Systems of planets have now been found orbiting stars other than our Sun.
The table shows the numbers of planets found in orbit around stars as of January 2013.

Number of planets	**Frequency**
2	65
3	18
4	5
5	3
6	1
7	1
8	1

a How many stars have been found with more than one planet in orbit?

....

b How many planets have been found in these systems?

....

c What is the modal number of planets?

....

4.4 Describe correlation in scatter graphs

GCSE LINKS
AF: 25.3 Recognising correlation; **BF:** Unit 1 4.5 Recognising correlation; **16+:** 22.2 Recognising correlation; **S:** 5.2 Correlation

By the end of this section you will know how to:

- Recognise the different types of correlation shown in a scatter graph
- Describe the different types of correlation shown in a scatter graph

Key points

- With **positive** correlation, as one variable **increases**, the other variable **increases**.
- With **negative** correlation, as one variable **increases**, the other variable **decreases**.
- With **strong correlation**, the points lie close to a straight line.
- With **weak correlation**, the points are scattered around the general direction of a line.
- If there is **no** correlation then as one variable **increases**, the other variable will show **no clear pattern** of increase or decrease.
- Figure 1 shows **strong positive** correlation.
- Figure 2 shows **weak negative** correlation.
- Figure 3 shows **no** correlation.

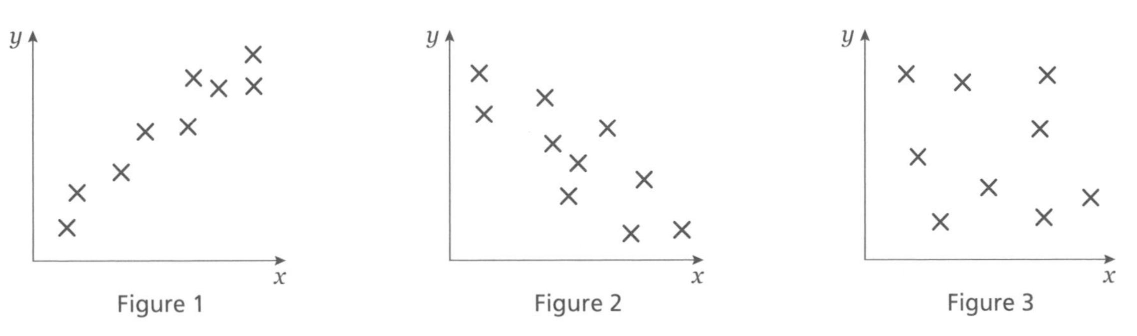

Figure 1 Figure 2 Figure 3

Guided

1 The scatter graph shows some information about the number of crimes committed in a city and their distance from the city centre.

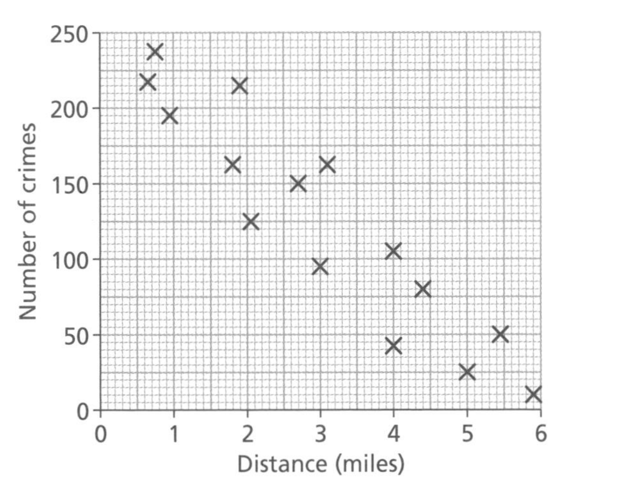

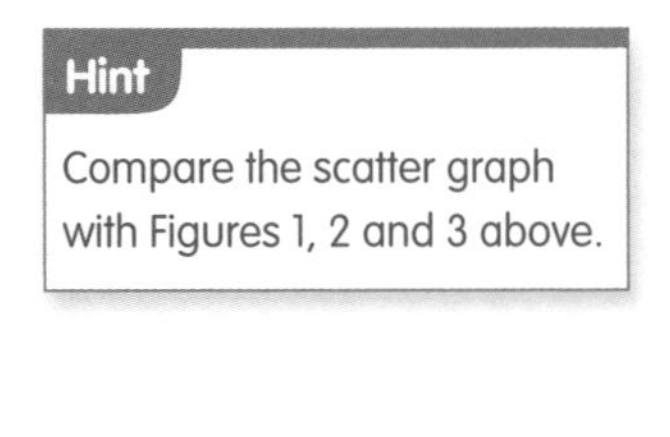

Hint
As you move to the right, does the number of crimes go up (increase) or down (decrease)?

Describe and interpret the correlation between the number of crimes and the distance from the city centre.

The scatter graph shows .... correlation.

As the distance from the centre increases, the number of crimes ....

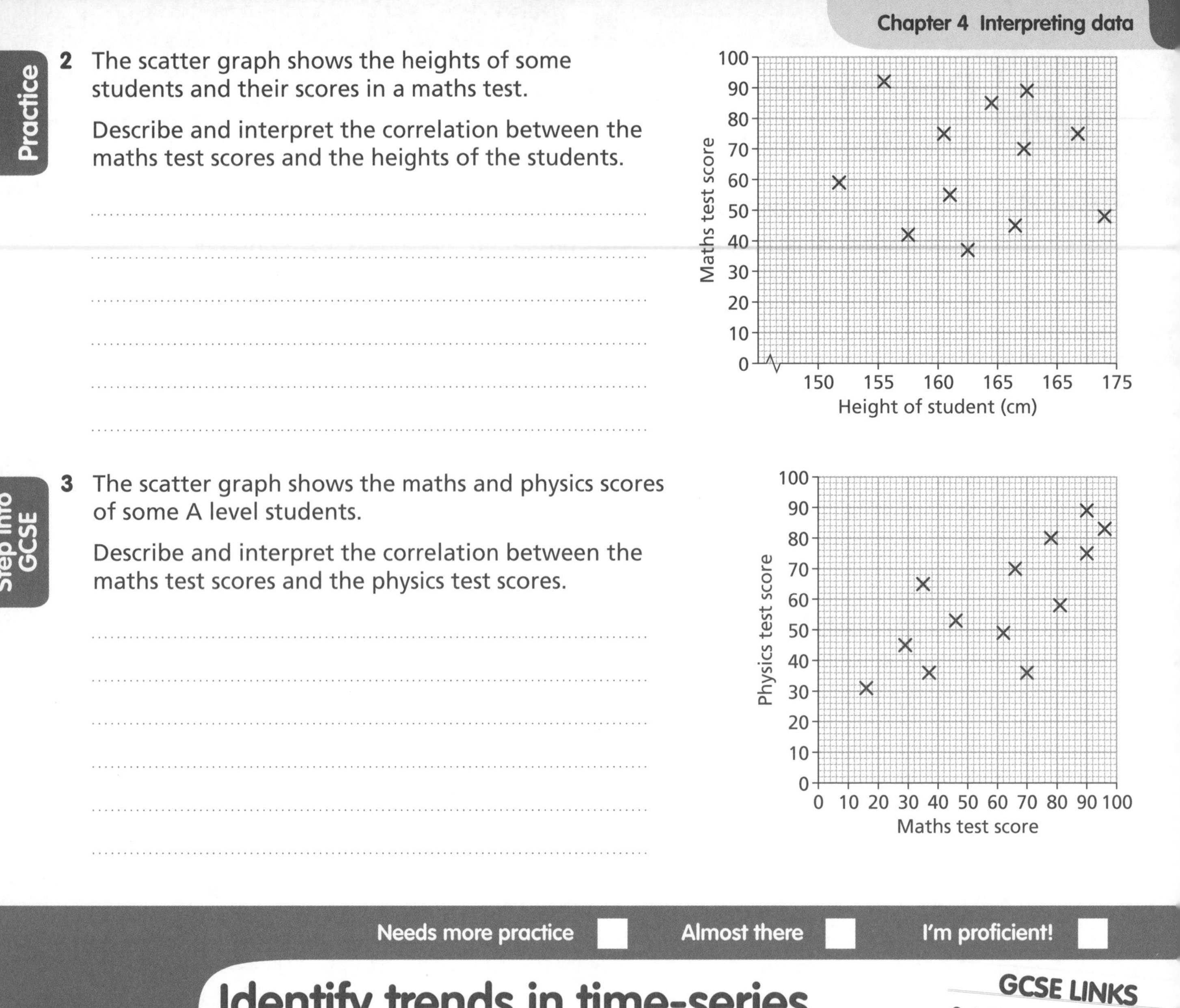

2 The scatter graph shows the heights of some students and their scores in a maths test.

Describe and interpret the correlation between the maths test scores and the heights of the students.

....

....

....

....

....

....

3 The scatter graph shows the maths and physics scores of some A level students.

Describe and interpret the correlation between the maths test scores and the physics test scores.

....

....

....

....

....

....

Needs more practice ☐ Almost there ☐ I'm proficient! ☐

Identify trends in time-series graphs

GCSE LINKS
S: 6.4 Variations in time series

By the end of this section you will know how to:

* Use a time-series graph to identify a trend.

Key points

* Trend will either be **upwards**, **downwards** or **level**.
* Figure 1 shows a typical **upward** trend.
* Figure 2 shows a typical **downward** trend.
* Figure 3 shows a typical **level** trend.

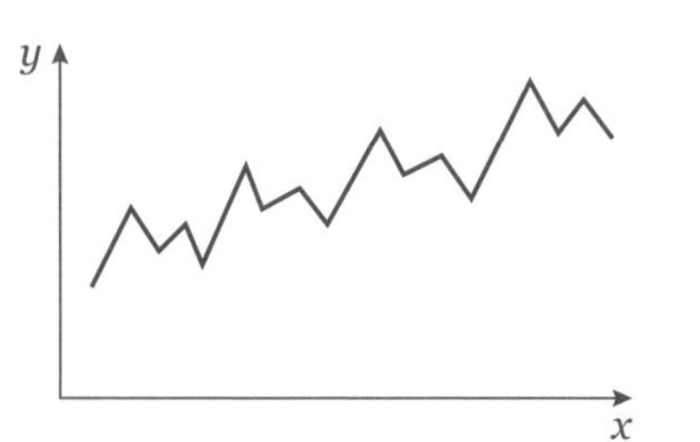

Figure 1

Figure 2

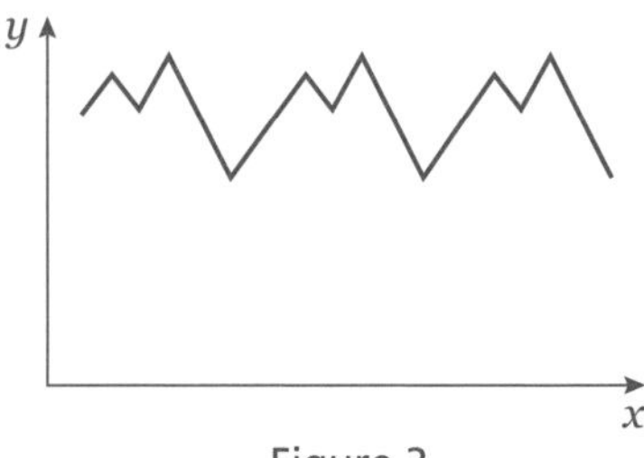

Figure 3

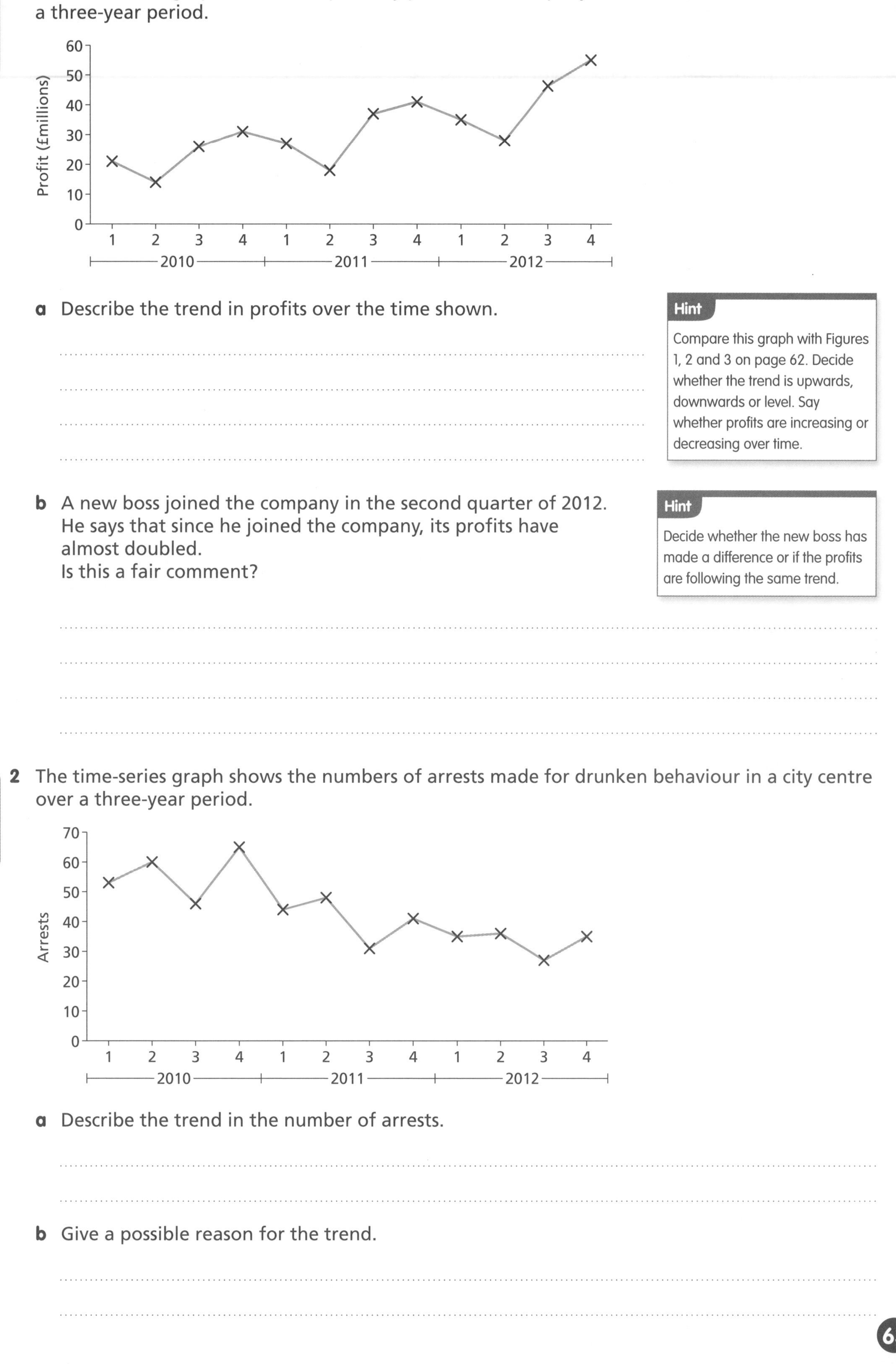

Guided

1 The time-series graph shows the quarterly profits of a company over a three-year period.

a Describe the trend in profits over the time shown.

....

....

....

....

Hint

Compare this graph with Figures 1, 2 and 3 on page 62. Decide whether the trend is upwards, downwards or level. Say whether profits are increasing or decreasing over time.

b A new boss joined the company in the second quarter of 2012. He says that since he joined the company, its profits have almost doubled.
Is this a fair comment?

Hint

Decide whether the new boss has made a difference or if the profits are following the same trend.

....

....

....

....

Practice

2 The time-series graph shows the numbers of arrests made for drunken behaviour in a city centre over a three-year period.

a Describe the trend in the number of arrests.

....

....

b Give a possible reason for the trend.

....

....

Step into GCSE

3 The time-series graph shows how the average house price in the UK has been changing since 1975.

a Describe the trend in house prices from 1975 to 1990.

....

....

....

....

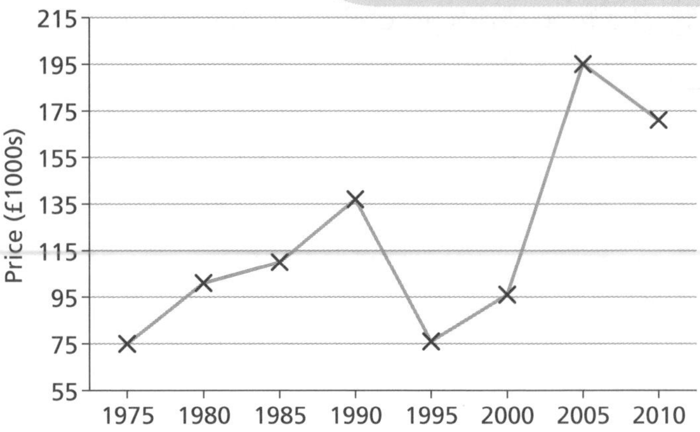

b Describe the trend in house prices from 1975 to 2010.

....

....

c When was the worst time to buy a house? Explain your answer.

....

....

....

Needs more practice ☐ Almost there ☐ I'm proficient! ☐

4.6 Compare data

By the end of this section you will know how to:

* Compare data using frequencies, totals, means, modes, medians and the range

Key points

* To compare two sets of data you can:
  - compare the **frequencies** of particular items
  - compare **totals**
  - choose the **mean**, **mode** or **median** and compare its value for each set
  - compare the **spread** of the data using the **range**.

Guided

1 The table shows how many bags of crisps of the top-selling flavours were sold at a shop on a Wednesday and on a Saturday.

	Frequency	
Flavour	**Wednesday**	**Saturday**
Cheese and onion	7	16
Prawn cocktail	3	9
Ready salted	10	8
Salt and vinegar	8	14
Smokey bacon	6	10
Total		

a Complete the table.

Hint
Find the totals for Wednesday and Saturday.

b How many more packets of crisps were sold on Saturday than Wednesday?

Hint
Use your answers to part **a**.

....

c Sales of one of the flavours on Saturday seem lower than expected.

i Which flavour is this? ....

ii Give a possible reason.

Hint
Do you always get what you ask for?

....

....

....

....

2 The table shows the numbers of days of sunshine in the UK and in Spain between April and August one year.

	Frequency	
Month	**UK**	**Spain**
April	11	23
May	15	26
June	21	28
July	19	27
August	17	22
Total		

a Complete the table.

b How many more days of sunshine were there in Spain than the UK?

....

c Which month was the sunniest in the UK?

....

d In which month did Spain have fewest sunny days?

....

Step into GCSE

3 The table shows the sales of motorbike accessories at a shop in April.

Item	Frequency
Helmets	36
Gloves	67
Jackets	44
Boots	31

In January, the shop only sold one third as many helmets, 10 fewer pairs of boots, the same number of jackets and 89 pairs of gloves.

a How many helmets were sold in January? ....

b How many boots were sold in January? ....

c How many more pairs of gloves were sold in January than April?

....

d Give a possible reason why the shop sold more gloves but fewer helmets in January compared with April.

....

....

....

....

Guided

4 Tom and Jerry play a round of crazy golf.
They keep track of the number of shots taken for each hole.
Here are Tom's results.

3 4 1 6 5 3 4 6

a Jerry's mean number of shots is 4.5 and his range is 3.
Compare the scores for Tom and Jerry.

Hint
Work out the mean and the range of Tom's scores. Compare the answers with Jerry's mean and range.

You should know
To work out the mean, add the scores and divide by the number of them.

You should know
To work out the range, take the smallest value from the largest.

....

....

....

....

....

....

b Who won the game?
Explain your answer.

Hint
Think about the mean values.

....

....

c Who was more consistent?
Explain your answer.

Hint
Think about the range for both players.

....

....

Practice

5 Sara and Elise play for a ladies cricket team.
Here are the numbers of runs that Sara made in each of the first five matches.

23 32 21 10 44

Elise scored a mean of 27.4 runs with a range of 22.

a Compare the results for Sara and Elise.

....

....

....

....

....

....

b Who has more runs so far? Explain your answer.

....

....

c Who is the more consistent player? Explain your answer.

....

....

GCSE

6 Fran and Megan are hairdressers. Some customers leave them cash tips. In one week Fran had these amounts in tips.

£3.50 £8.25 £2 £12 £4.25

In the same week, Megan had a mean of £5.80 per day with a range of £7.

a Compare the tips for Fran and Megan.

....

....

....

....

....

....

b Who had more tips for the week? Explain your answer.

....

....

c Whose tips were more variable? Explain your answer.

....

....

Guided

7 Steve and Sheryl each made a paper aeroplane.
They each had five attempts at flying their aeroplane as far as possible.
Here are Steve's results in metres to the nearest whole number.

2 5 3 11 6

Sheryl's median distance was 6 m and her range was 4 m.

You should know

The median is the middle number when the data is in order.

a Compare Steve and Sheryl's results.

....

....

....

....

b Who achieved the most consistent distances?
Explain your answer.

Hint

Think about the range values.

....

....

Practice

8 The Passquick and Passmaster driving schools are in competition.
Here are the numbers of lessons that some Passquick clients took to pass the test.

24 30 26 27 32 40 28 48

The median number of lessons for Passmaster is 29.5 and the range is 16.

a Compare the two companies.

....

....

....

....

b Which company would you choose?
Give a reason.

....

....

....

....

Step into GCSE

9 Lizzy and Sam compare their favourite movies.
They each give a mark out of 10 for every movie on their list.
Here are Lizzy's scores.

7 7 9 10 7 8

Sam's scores have a median of 8 and a range of 4.
Make two comparisons of the scores.

1 ....

2 ....

Guided

10 The Cobras and the Bulldogs are two basketball teams.
Here are the heights of the Cobras team players in centimetres.

188 186 188 185 190 186 188 192

The modal height of the Bulldogs team is 190 cm and the range is 8 cm.

You should know

The modal height is the height that occurs most often.

a Compare the heights of the two teams.

....

....

....

....

b Which team is more consistent in height?
Explain your answer.

Hint

Think about the range values.

....

....

Practice

11 Robin and Marion are archers. They each have eight arrows to aim at a target with a maximum possible score of 10 for each shot. Robin's scores are:

8 10 9 9 7 9 10 8

The mode of Marion's scores is 9 and her lowest score is 8.
The winner is the one with the higher mode.
If the modes are equal then the one with the lower range is the winner.
Who wins? Explain your answer.

....

....

....

....

GCSE

12 Jeremy counted the number of vehicles passing through some traffic lights each time the lights changed.
Here are the numbers that Jeremy wrote down.

11 9 8 9 10 9 7 10 9 12

He found that the numbers of vehicles travelling in the opposite direction had a modal value of 15 and a range of 5.

a Compare the two sets of data.

....

....

....

....

b The lights seem to let more vehicles though in one direction than the other.
Give a possible reason for this.

....

....

....

....

Needs more practice ☐ Almost there ☐ I'm proficient! ☐

4.7 Make comparisons and predictions from data and representations of data

By the end of this section you will know how to:

* Compare data using pie charts and time-series graphs
* Make predictions using scatter graphs and time-series graphs

Key points

* Pie charts can be used to compare proportions.
* Time-series graphs can be used to make comparisons over a period of time.
* Scatter graphs and time-series graphs can be used to make predictions.

Guided

1 David and Calvin play football for two different teams. The pie charts show how their teams performed.

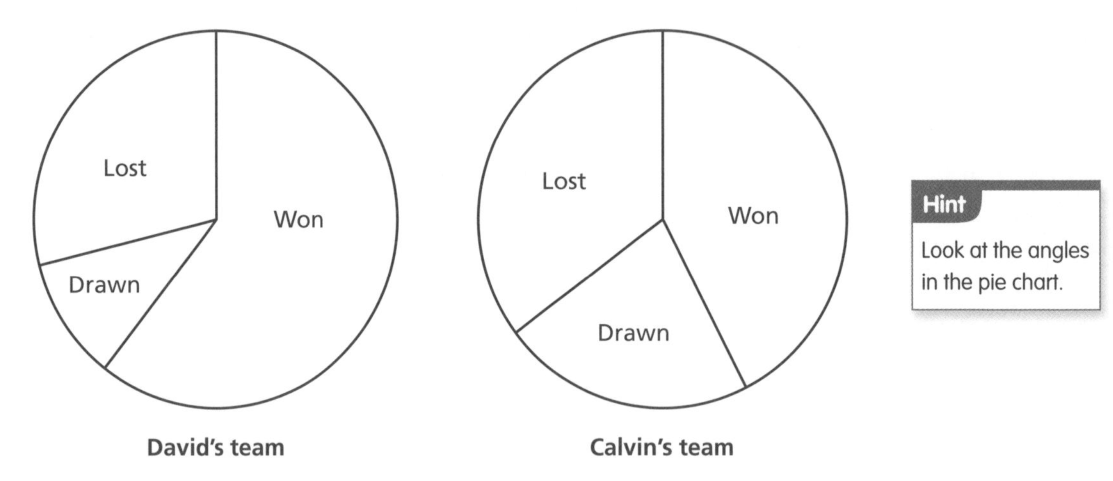

Hint
Look at the angles in the pie chart.

a Did David's team win, lose or draw most of the matches they played? Explain your answer.

....

....

b Calvin says that his team won more matches than they lost or drew put together. Is this true? Explain your answer.

Hint
Look at the total angle for Lost and Drawn.

....

....

Calvin's team played twice as many matches as David's team.

Hint
David's team needs twice the angle for the same number of matches as Calvin's.

c Which team lost more matches? ....

d Which team won more matches? Explain your answer.

....

....

....

....

Practice

2 Some Year 9 students were asked to estimate the proportions of students staying on at school, going to college or starting work at the end of Year 11.
The pie charts show their estimates and the actual results for a Year 11 group.

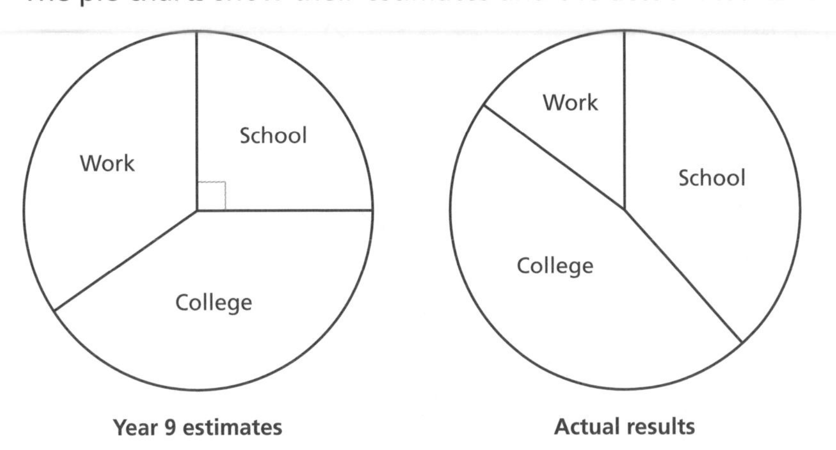

Year 9 estimates **Actual results**

a Which proportion did the Year 9 students over-estimate? Explain your answer.

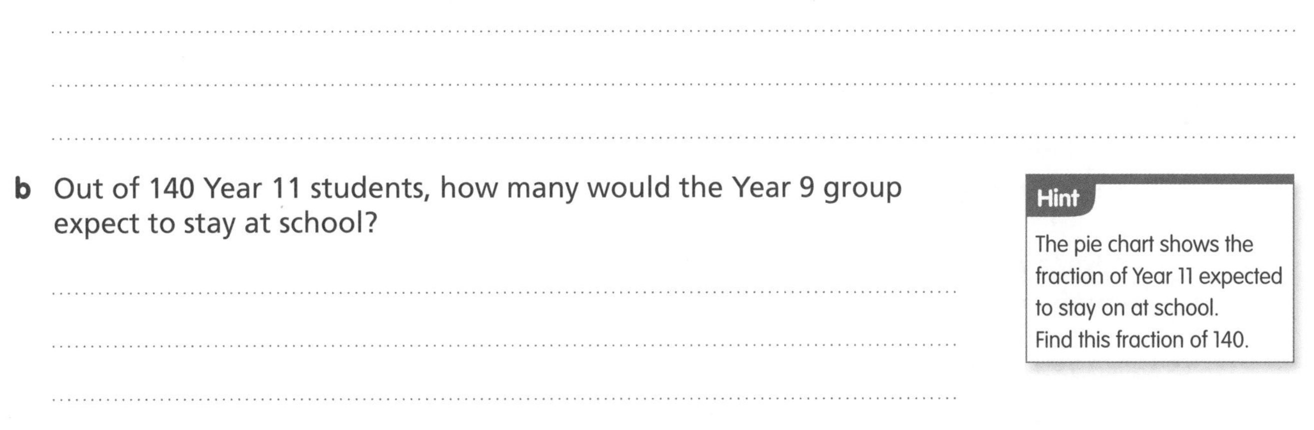

b Out of 140 Year 11 students, how many would the Year 9 group expect to stay at school?

Hint
The pie chart shows the fraction of Year 11 expected to stay on at school.
Find this fraction of 140.

c Which is the most popular destination for students at the end of Year 11? ....

GCSE

3 The pie charts show how the average weight of adult Americans has changed in the last 50 years.

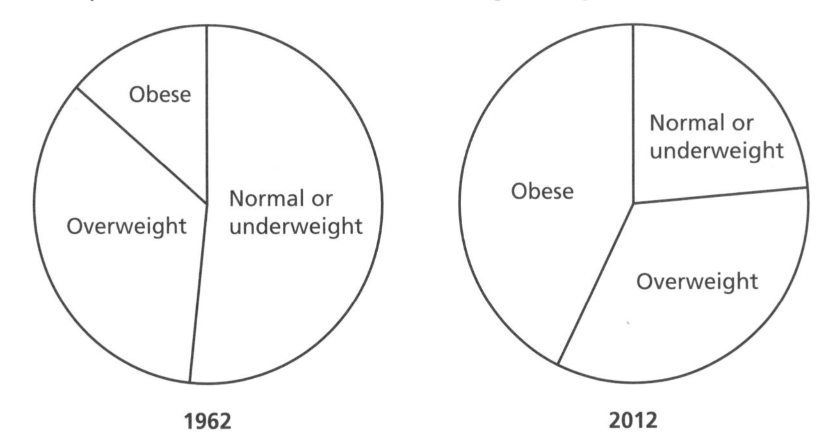

1962 **2012**

a Which category was the largest in 1962? ....

b Which category was the largest in 2012? ....

c Describe the changes between 1962 and 2012.

Guided

4 The time-series graph shows the rates of inflation in the US and the UK between 2003 and 2011.

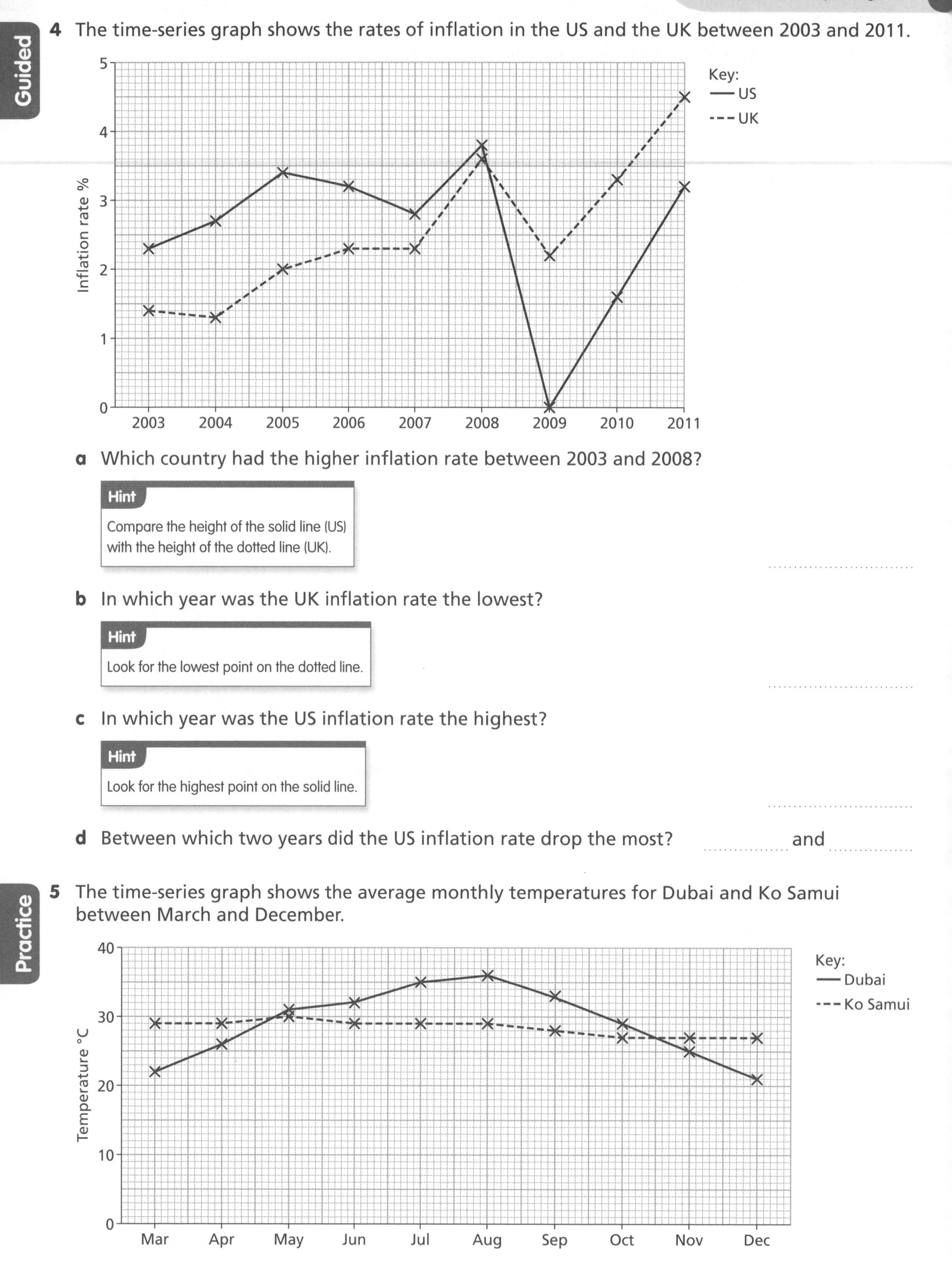

a Which country had the higher inflation rate between 2003 and 2008?

> **Hint**
> Compare the height of the solid line (US) with the height of the dotted line (UK).

....

b In which year was the UK inflation rate the lowest?

> **Hint**
> Look for the lowest point on the dotted line.

....

c In which year was the US inflation rate the highest?

> **Hint**
> Look for the highest point on the solid line.

....

d Between which two years did the US inflation rate drop the most? .... and ....

Practice

5 The time-series graph shows the average monthly temperatures for Dubai and Ko Samui between March and December.

a How much warmer is Ko Samui than Dubai in March?

.... °C

b In which month is the temperature highest in Dubai?

....

c Find the range of temperatures for Ko Samui.

.... °C

d Find the range of temperatures for Dubai.

.... °C

e If you wanted to go somewhere hot in January, do you think it would be better to go to Dubai or Ko Samui? Give a reason for your answer.

....

....

....

....

....

GCSE

6 The time-series graph shows how the average prices of similar properties changed in two different regions.

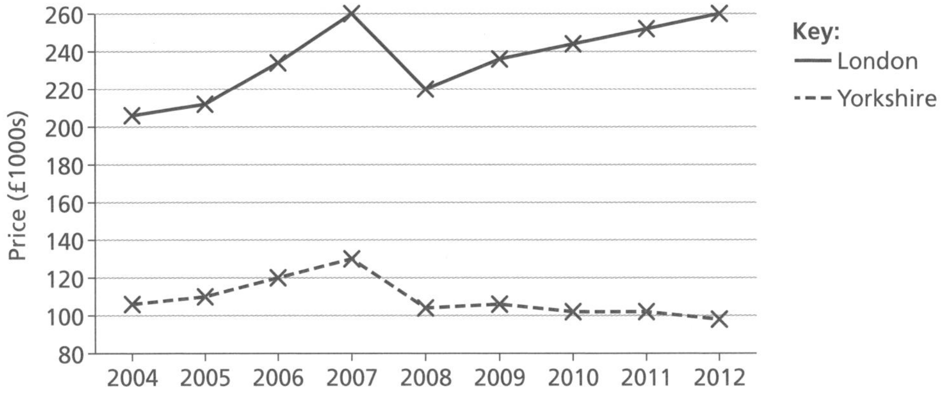

Price (£1000s)

260 240 220 200 180 160 140 120 100 80

2004 2005 2006 2007 2008 2009 2010 2011 2012

Key:

—— London

- - - Yorkshire

a What was happening to house prices in London and Yorkshire between 2004 and 2007?

....

....

b What happened to the prices between 2007 and 2008?

....

c Describe the difference between London house prices and Yorkshire house prices since 2008.

....

....

....

....

Guided

7 A survey in the area of San Francisco showed big differences in the amount of crime per month depending on the distance from the city centre. The data is shown on the scatter graph.

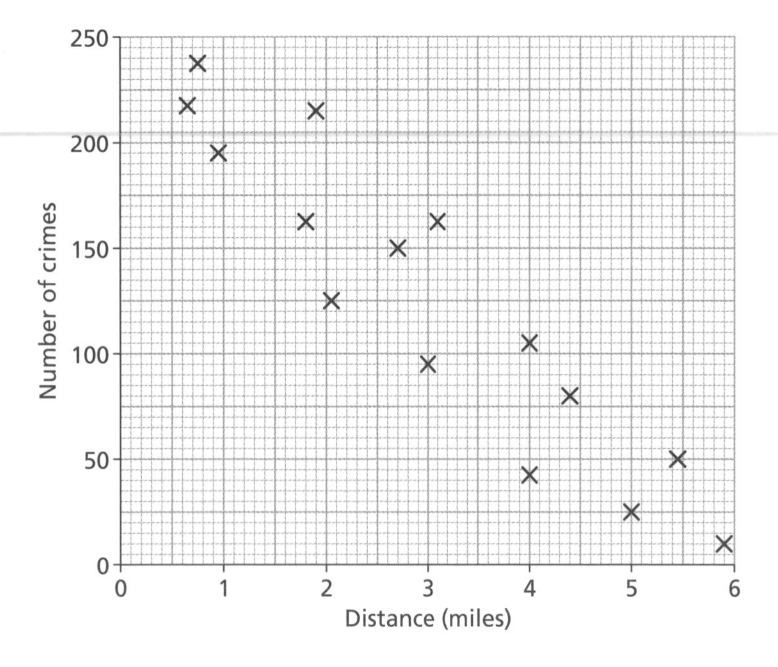

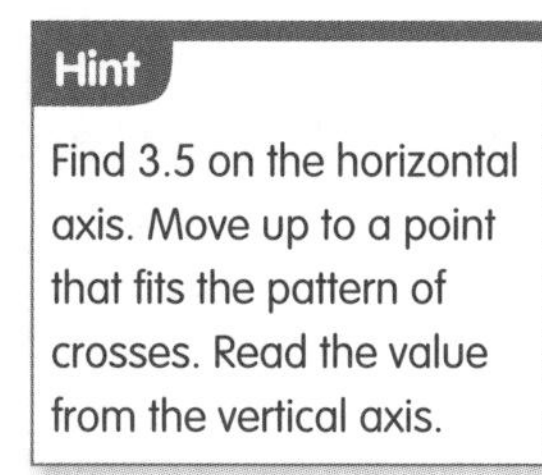

Sally is thinking of renting an apartment 3.5 miles from the centre of San Francisco.
Use the diagram to estimate the number of crimes per month in that area.

....

Practice

8 The scatter graph shows the scores on Paper 1 and Paper 2 of a maths test for a group of students.

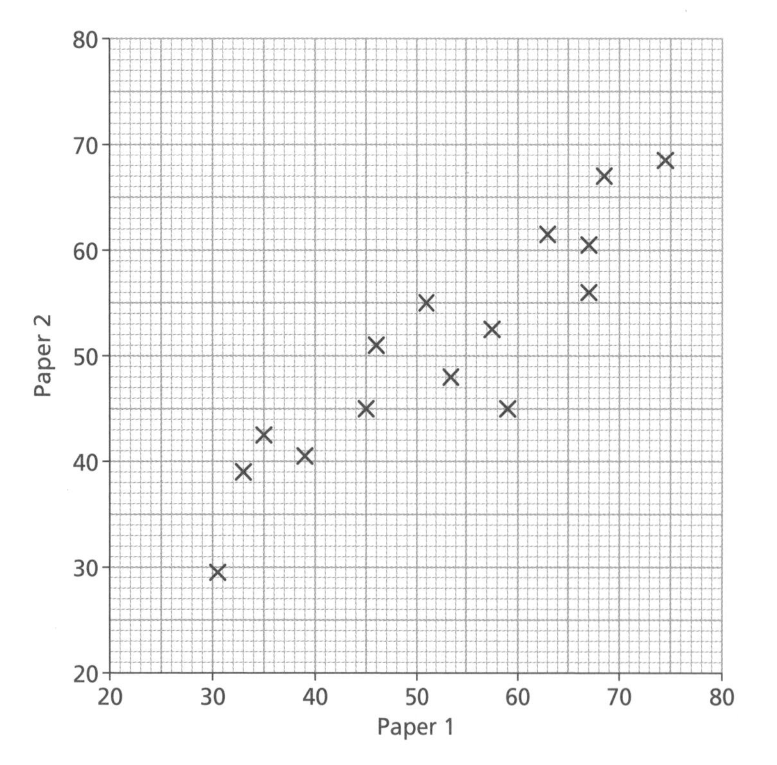

Andrew missed Paper 2 but scored 65 marks on Paper 1.
Use the diagram to find an estimated mark for Andrew on Paper 2.

....

GCSE

9 Mike has been studying the movement of vehicles approaching traffic lights. He noticed that when the lights change to green, each vehicle in the queue is delayed an amount of time before it can move. The scatter graph shows his results.

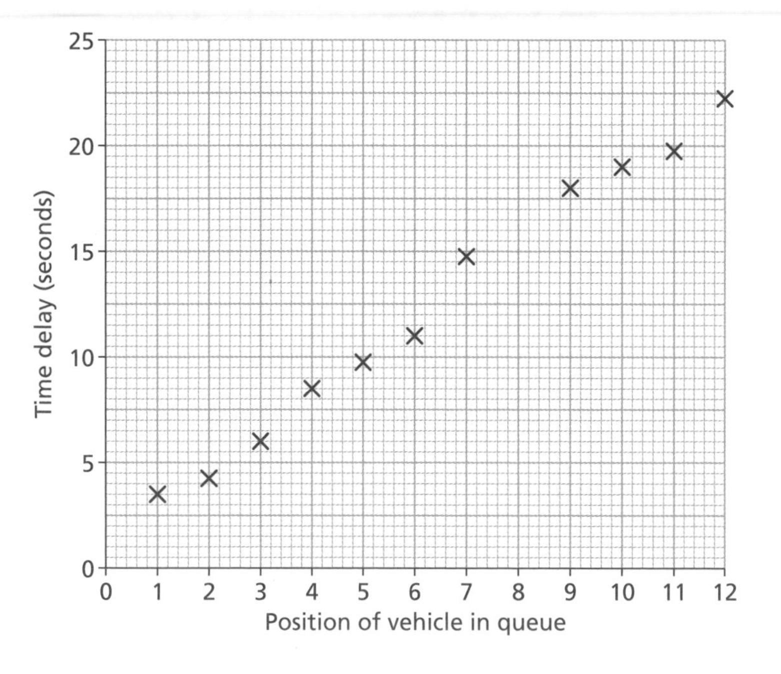

Mike missed the time for the eighth vehicle. Use the graph to estimate the delay.

.... seconds

Guided

10 The time-series graph is intended to show the number of units sold at a factory each quarter for three years.

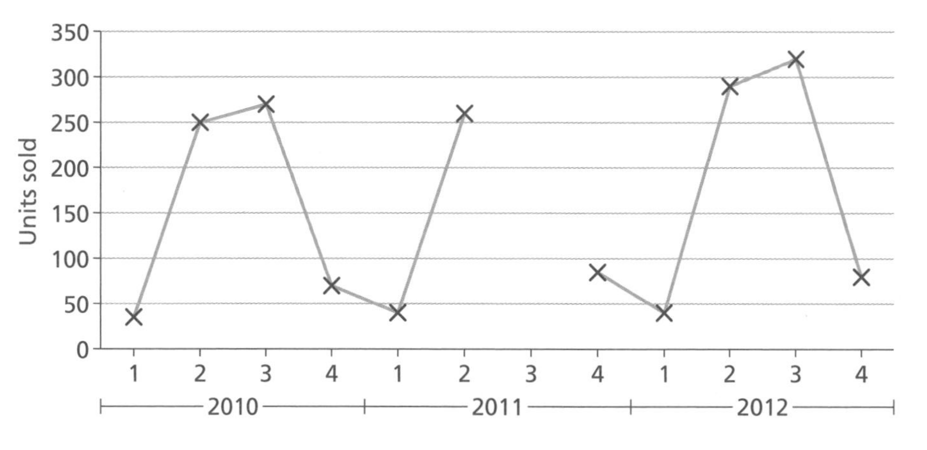

The value for the third quarter of 2011 is not known.
Complete the graph to show an estimate for the missing value.

Hint
Look at the pattern for each year and follow the trend.

11 The average monthly temperatures at a resort were recorded over a season.
This information is shown on the time-series graph but one value is missing.

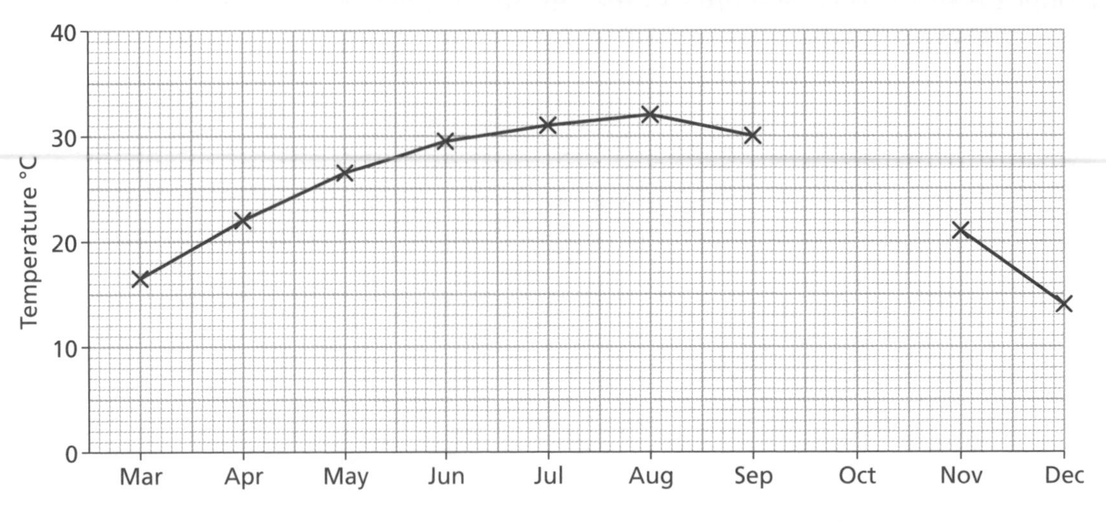

Complete the graph to show an estimate of the temperature for October.

Step into GCSE

12 The time-series graph shows the numbers of umbrellas sold at a shop in Manchester over one year.

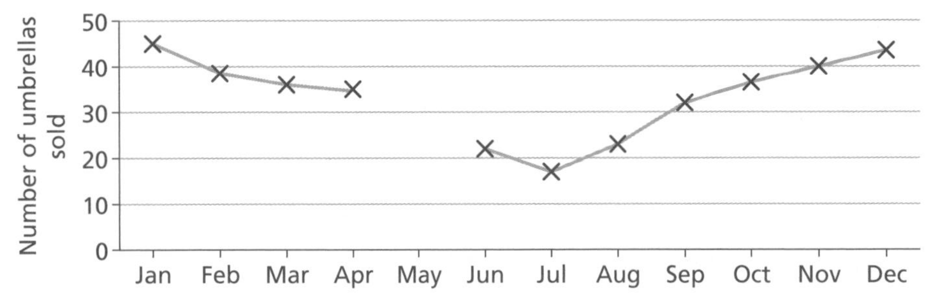

The information for May is missing.
Complete the graph to show an estimate of the number of umbrellas sold in May.

Don't forget!

- Use the .... or description of the diagram to find out what it is about.
- Look at the labels and try to compare values or look for a ....
- On a scatter graph:
  - if as one variable increases the other increases, the correlation is ....
  - if as one variable increases the other decreases, the correlation is ....
  - if as one variable increases the other varies without a pattern, there is ....
- You may need to add an extra row or column to a frequency table to find the ....
- The mode is the value that occurs with the .... frequency.
- You can use a .... graph to identify a trend.
- You can use an average and the .... to compare sets of data.
- You can use pie charts to compare ....
- You can use time-series graphs to make comparisons over a period of ....
- You can use scatter graphs and .... graphs to make predictions.

Exam-style questions

1 The table shows the final medal count for the top six countries in the 2012 Olympics.

Country	Gold	Silver	Bronze	Total
United States of America	46	29	29	
People's Republic of China	38	27	23	88
Great Britain	29	17	19	
Russian Federation	24	26	32	82
Republic of Korea	13	8		28
Germany		19	14	44

a Complete the table by filling in the missing values.

b The Russian Federation had a higher medal count than Great Britain.
Explain why Great Britain is above the Russian Federation in the table.

....

....

c Find the difference in the total number of medals between the top two countries.

....

2 The table shows the distances in miles between six places in the UK.

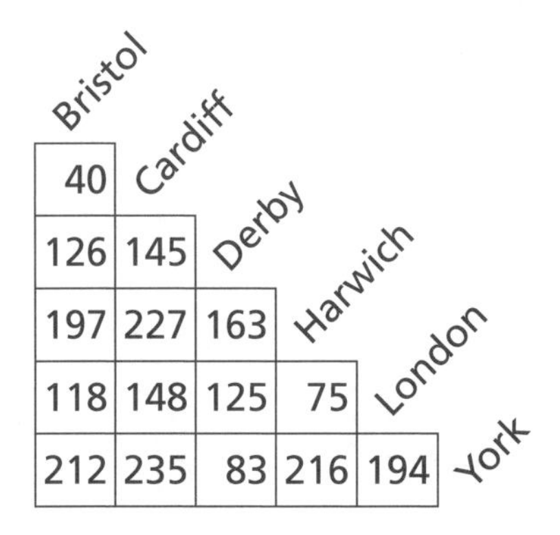

	Bristol	Cardiff	Derby	Harwich	London
Cardiff	40				
Derby	126	145			
Harwich	197	227	163		
London	118	148	125	75	
York	212	235	83	216	194

a How far is it from Cardiff to York? .... miles

b Which city is 197 miles from Harwich? ....

c Kate drives from London to Cardiff and then on to Derby.
How far does she drive altogether?

.... miles

3 The pictogram shows the numbers of visitors to a sea-life centre in one week.

Monday	○ ◐
Tuesday	
Wednesday	○ ○ ○ ◐
Thursday	○ ○ ○ ○ ○
Friday	○ ○ ○ ○ ◔
Saturday	○ ○ ○ ○ ○ ○ ◐

Key:
○ represents 400 people

a How many visitors were there on Monday? ....

b There were 700 visitors on Tuesday. Complete the pictogram.

c How many more visitors were there on Thursday than on Friday?

....

4 Sports clubs in the UK report an increase in membership since the Olympic and Paralympic Games. The dual bar chart shows how the membership of some clubs has changed.

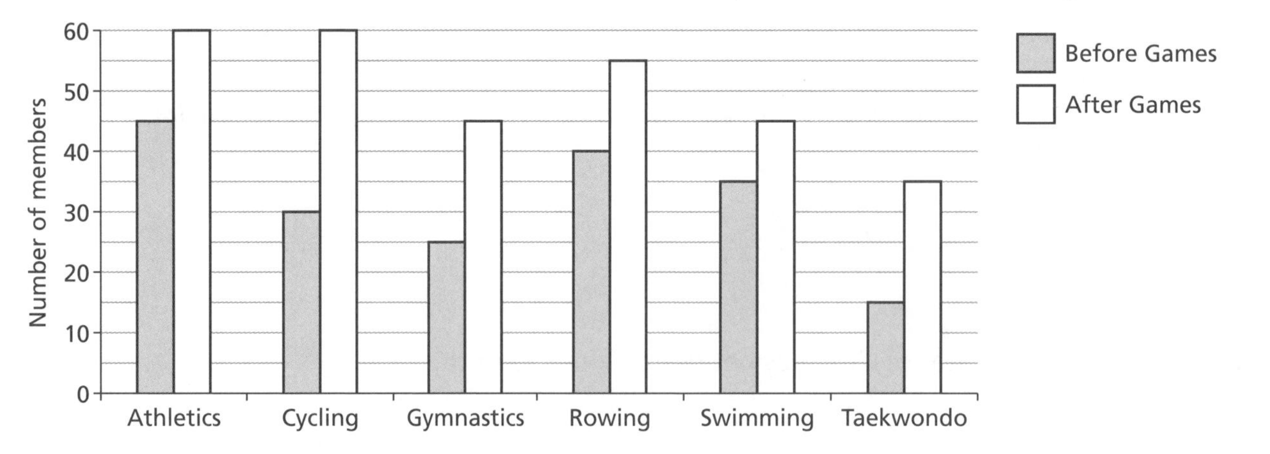

a Which club had the largest increase in membership numbers? ....

b Which club more than doubled its membership? ....

c How many more people are now in the gymnastics club? ....

5 The table shows the numbers of A levels studied by a group of 40 students.

Number of A levels	Frequency
1	2
2	5
3	18
4	12
5	

a Complete the table.

b What is the modal number of A levels studied? ....

c What is the range in the number of A levels studied? ....

6 Harry measured the girth and height of some trees in a park.
The scatter graph shows his results.

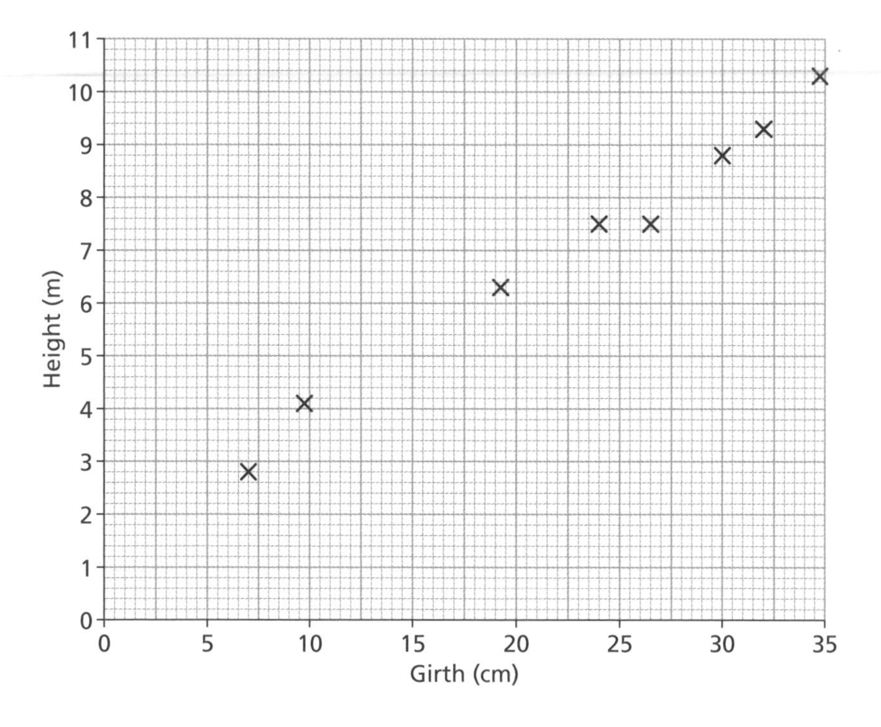

a What type of correlation does the graph show? ....

b Use the diagram to estimate the height of a tree with girth 15 cm. .... m

7 A fairground stall has six cans placed on a wall. Players have three bean bags and try to knock down as many cans as possible. All six cans must be knocked down to win a prize.
The table shows the results for a group of players. Each player only played once.

Number of cans	Frequency	
1	0	
2	1	
3	3	
4	4	
5	8	
6	10	

a How many players were there? ....

b How many prizes were won? ....

c How many cans were knocked down altogether?

....

8 The time-series graph shows the percentages of students gaining a Grade C or better in GCSE Maths and English.

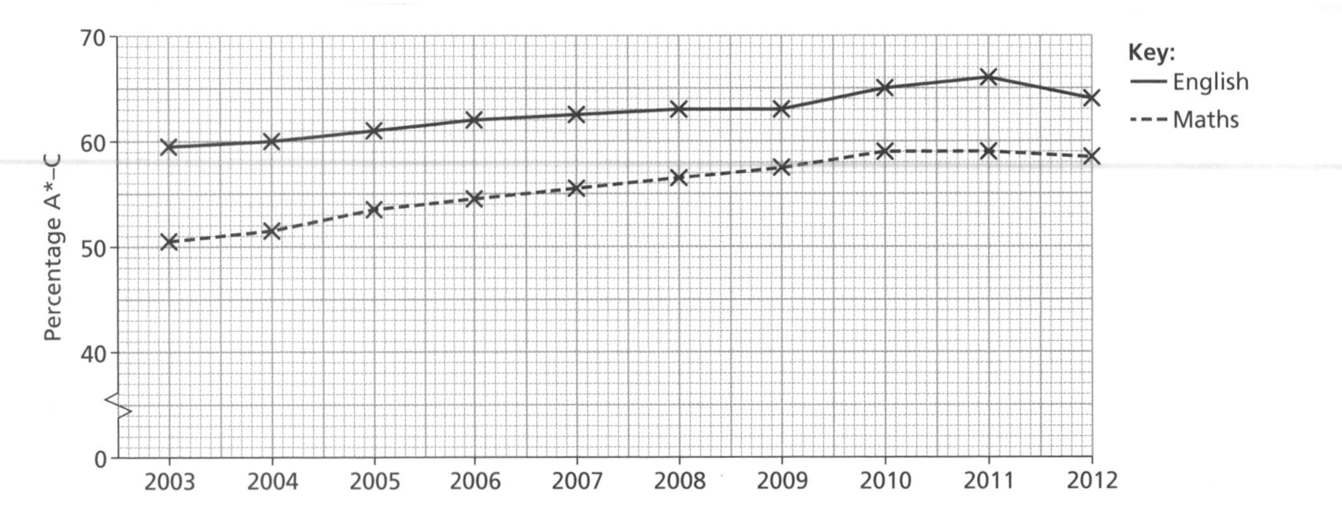

Use the diagram to make **three** comparisons between the Maths and English results.

1 ....

....

2 ....

....

3 ....

....

9 Describe the type of correlation shown in each of these scatter graphs.

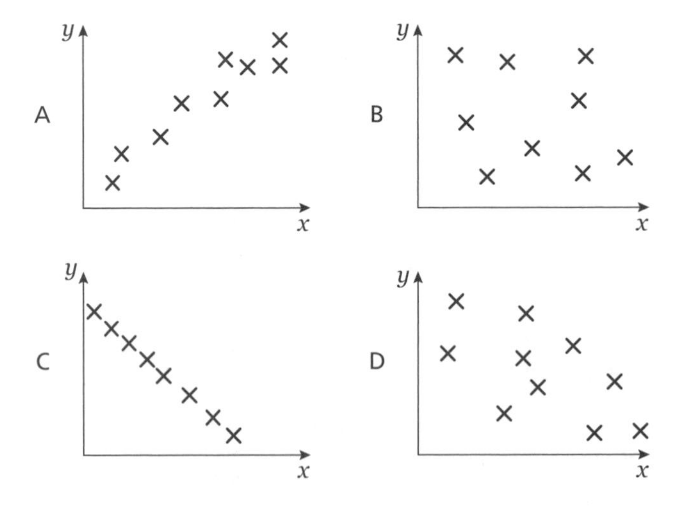

A ....

B ....

C ....

D ....

5.1 Use and interpret a probability scale

GCSE LINKS
AF: 26.1 The probability scale; **BF:** Unit 1 5.1 The probability scale; **S:** 7.2 The meaning of probability

By the end of this section you will know how to:

* Use the probability scale to represent probabilities

Key points

It is useful to think about an example of a probability experiment, such as rolling a dice, to understand the words used in probability.

* The probability experiment (in this case rolling the dice once) is called a **trial**.
* The result of the probability experiment (in this case, getting a score from 1 to 6) is called an **outcome**.
* A particular set of outcomes, such as scoring 2, 4 or 6 is an **event**.
* The **probability** of an event is a measure of how likely it will happen.
* If an event is **impossible**, the probability that it will happen is **0**. (For example, it is impossible to get a 7 on an ordinary dice, so the probability is 0.)
* If an event is **certain**, the probability that it will happen is **1**. (For example, it is certain that you will get one of the numbers 1, 2, 3, 4, 5, 6 on an ordinary dice, so the probability is 1.)
* The probability of any event must lie on a scale from 0 to 1, including the values 0 and 1.
* An event that is just as likely **not** to happen as it is to happen has an **even** chance. The probability of an event with an even chance is $\frac{1}{2}$. You can also write this as 0.5 or 50%.

Guided

1 Here is a probability scale.

Choose the most suitable word from the probability scale to describe the probability of each of these events.

a A fair coin will land heads up when spun. Evens

Hint The coin is just as likely to land heads up as tails up.

b It will snow in Birmingham in April. ....

Hint The weather normally gets warmer by April, but it can get cold.

c A baby will be born today. ....

Hint It has been estimated that a baby is born every 4 seconds.

d A cow will write a poem. ....

Practice

2 Use the same probability scale as in Question 1. Find the most suitable word to describe the probability of each of these events.

Hint In a pack of playing cards, 26 are red and 26 are black.

a An ordinary dice is rolled and the score shown is greater than 2. ....

b A red card is selected, without looking, from a full pack of playing cards. ....

c A husband and wife like **all** of the same television programmes. ....

Guided

3 The probability scale shows the positions of events A, B and C.

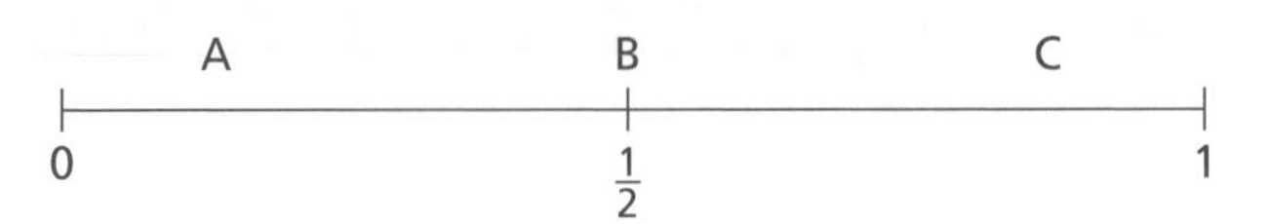

Write down the letter that gives the best match to the probability of each of these events. (You can use each letter more than once.)

Hint

Choose A if you think the event is very unlikely, choose B if you think the event has an even chance and C if you think it is very likely to happen.

a The first person to walk into a shop in London in January is wearing a coat. ....

b As you approach three different sets of traffic lights in a car, they each turn green. ....

c I pick a horse in a race because it has a funny name, and it wins. ....

d You roll an ordinary six-sided dice and score an even number. ....

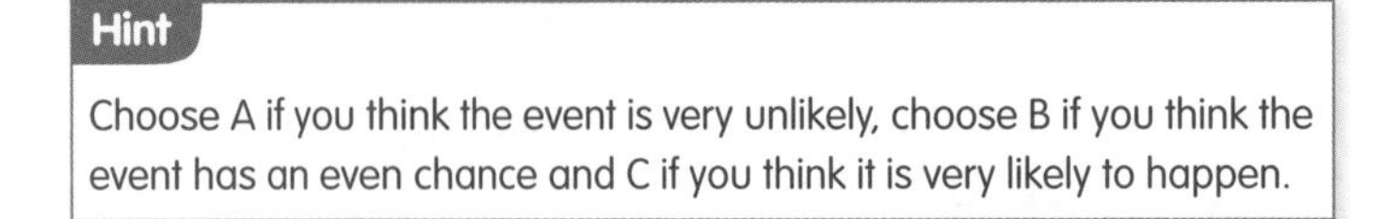

Practice

4 Here is a probability scale.

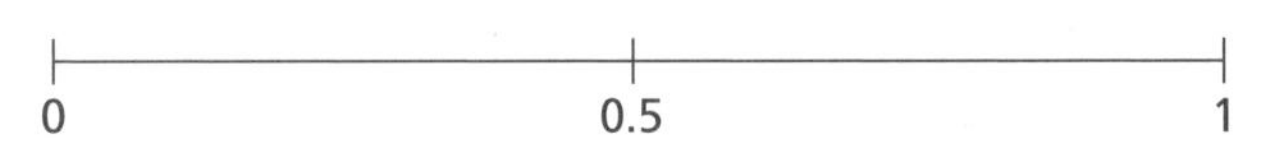

a Label the point A on the scale to show the probability that the first baby born at a maternity unit is a girl.

b Label the point B on the scale to show the probability that it will be sunny every day of the next school summer holidays where you live.

c Label the point C on the scale to show the probability that a new Olympic record will be set in some event at the next Olympics.

Step into GCSE

5 Here are some events.

A The next person you meet was born in a leap year.

B You will walk from Lands End to John O'Groats in one day.

C A person landing at an airport for a holiday has a suitcase to collect.

D Six girls and four boys put their names into a hat.

The first name pulled out is a girl's name.

Write A, B, C or D in each box on the probability scale to show how likely the event is to happen.

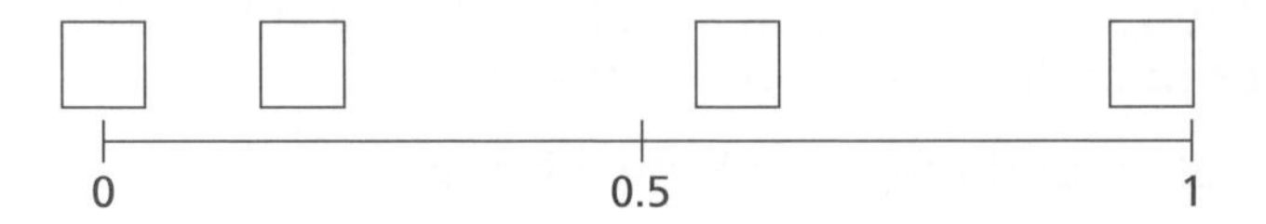

Needs more practice ☐ Almost there ☐ I'm proficient! ☐

5.2 Write down theoretical and experimental probabilities

GCSE LINKS
AF: 26.2 Writing probabilities as numbers; **BF:** Unit 1 5.2 Writing probabilities as numbers; **16+:** 23.1 Working out the probability of events happening **S:** 7.3 The probability of an event

By the end of this section you will know how to:

* Find the theoretical probability of an event
* Find the relative frequency of an event

Key points

* If something is taken **at random** from a collection of objects, each object has the same chance of being taken, i.e. it is **equally likely**.
* When all of the possible outcomes are equally likely, the **probability** of an event is:

  Probability of an event = $\frac{\text{The number of outcomes in the event}}{\text{The total number of outcomes}}$

* If the outcomes are not equally likely, the probability may be estimated by experiment using **relative frequency**.
* In an experiment, the **relative frequency** of an event is:

  Relative frequency of an event = $\frac{\text{The number of trials where the event occurred}}{\text{The total number of trials}}$

* The relative frequency becomes more reliable as an estimate of probability as the number of trials is increased.

Remember this
An outcome is something that happens in an experiment such as a dice showing a score of 6.

Remember this
A trial is something that you do in an experiment, such as rolling a dice.

Equally likely outcomes

Guided

1 An ordinary six-sided dice is rolled once.

a The probability of a score of 5 is $\frac{1}{\dots\dots}$

Hint
There is 1 outcome in the event. There are 6 possible outcomes.

b The probability of an even score is ....

Hint
The outcomes in the event are 2, 4, 6.

c The probability of a score less than 5 is ....

Hint
The outcomes in the event are 1, 2, 3, 4. Notice that 5 is not included.

d The probability that the score is not 6 is ....

Hint
The outcomes in the event are 1, 2, 3, 4, 5.

e The probability of a score of 8 is ....

Hint
It's impossible to score 8.

Practice

2 The five-sided spinner is spun once.

a The probability that the spinner will land on green is ....

b The probability that the spinner will **not** land on green is ....

c The probability that the spinner will land on an odd number is ....

d The probability that the spinner will land on a white odd number is ....

e The probability that the spinner will land on a green even number is ....

1 5 4 2 3

Hint
There are five possible outcomes. Of these, two are green and three are white.

Guided

3 A jar contains sweets with different coloured wrappers.
The table shows the number of each colour.

Colour	Red	Blue	Green
Frequency	7	8	5

A sweet is selected at random.

a The probability that the sweet is blue is $\frac{8}{\dots\dots}$

Hint
Add the frequencies to get the total number of outcomes.

b Show your answer to part **a** on the probability scale.
Label the point A.

0 0.5 1

Hint
Each mark on the scale represents $\frac{1}{10}$ or 0.1.

c The probability that the sweet is not green is ....

Hint
The number of outcomes in the event is the total of red plus blue.

d Show your answer to part **c** on the probability scale.
Label the point C.

Practice

4 The table shows the results of a survey about choices of language to study at GCSE.
Each student can choose only one language.

	French	**German**	**Spanish**	**Total**
Boys	7	6	5	18
Girls	8	7	9	24
Total	15	13	14	42

One of these students is selected at random.

a The probability that the student is a boy is ....

b The probability that the student is a girl who chooses French is ....

c The probability that the student chooses Spanish is ....

5 The table shows some details of the cars for sale at a garage.

A car is selected at random.

	Engine size (litres)			
	1.2	**1.4**	**1.6**	**Total**
Diesel	1	2	4	7
Petrol	5	6	7	18
Total	6	8	11	25

a The probability that the car runs on diesel is ....

b The probability that the car has a 1.4 litre engine is ....

c The probability that the car has a 1.2 litre engine that runs on petrol is ....

Relative frequency

Guided

6 A drawing pin can land point up or point down. Karen drops a drawing pin 50 times. The table shows her results.

	Point up	Point down
Frequency	31	19

Hint
The total number of trials for this experiment is 50.

a The relative frequency that the drawing pin lands point up is $\frac{31}{\ldots\ldots}$

b The relative frequency that the drawing pin lands point down is ....

Practice

7 Kevin spins this spinner 40 times and records the results in a table.

Score	1	2	3	4
Frequency	8	4	5	23

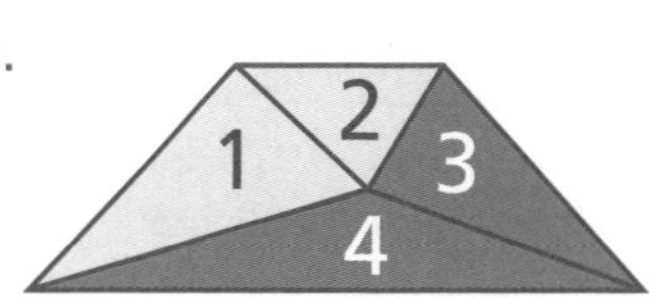

a The relative frequency of scoring 1 is ....

b The relative frequency of **not** scoring 4 is ....

c The relative frequency of landing on an dark sector is ....

Hint
Combine the frequencies for the two dark sectors.

GCSE

8 Megan rolls an ordinary six-sided dice 20 times. The table shows her results.

Score	1	2	3	4	5	6
Frequency	2	5	4	3	1	5

a Find the relative frequency of scoring 5. ....

b Find the relative frequency of scoring 6. ....

c Megan decides that she is much more likely to score 6 than 5.
Comment on Megan's decision.

....

....

d What could Megan do to improve the reliability of her results?

....

....

Needs more practice ☐ Almost there ☐ I'm proficient! ☐

5.3 Estimate probabilities from practical situations

By the end of this section you will know how to:

* Use relative frequency to estimate probability

GCSE LINKS
AF: 26.5 Relative frequency and 26.7 Predicting outcomes; **BF:** Unit 1 5.6 Relative frequency; 5.8 Predicting outcomes; **16+:** 23.4 Using relative frequency to estimate probability and predict results; **S:** 7.4 Experimental probability

Key points

* Repeating an experiment will usually produce **different** outcomes.
* Probabilities may be written as **fractions**, or **decimals** or **percentages**.

Guided

1 Kate plants 80 seeds and finds that 63 of them germinate.
Estimate the probability that a seed selected at random will germinate.
Give your answer as a decimal.

Hint
Use relative frequency.
63 out of 80 seeds germinate.
Work out 63 ÷ 80.

....

Practice

2 At a set of traffic lights, cars can only turn left or right. In a survey of 50 cars, 30 turned left.
Estimate the probability that the next car will turn left.
Give your answer as a decimal.

....

3 According to a website, a hotel has had 35 reviews and of these 21 rated it as Excellent.

a Estimate the probability that the next visitor will rate the hotel as Excellent.

....

b Write your answer to part **a** as a percentage.

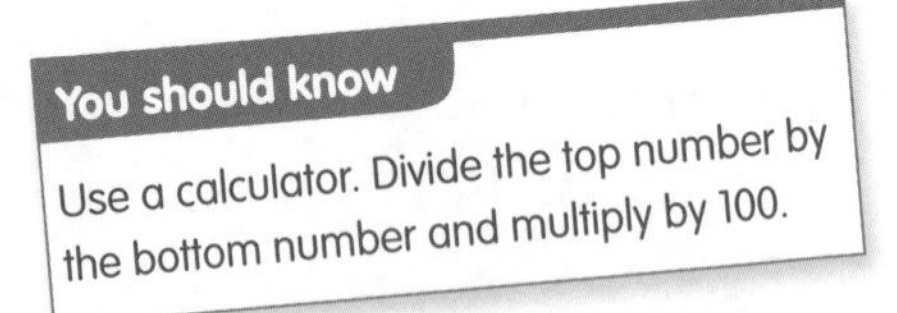

You should know
Use a calculator. Divide the top number by the bottom number and multiply by 100.

....

Step into GCSE

4 Rob is thinking about having an operation to improve his sight. The surgeon has previously carried out 75 similar operations and in 66 of the cases there was a significant improvement.

a Estimate the probability that Rob's eyesight will be improved by the operation.

....

b Write your answer to part **a** as a percentage. ....

c Another surgeon has had a 100% success rate. Explain why this surgeon isn't necessarily better.

....

....

5.4 Add probabilities

GCSE LINKS
16+: 23.2 Probability of events not happening; S: 7.7 Mutually exclusive events

By the end of this section you will know how to:

* Add probabilities
* Work out the probability that an event will not happen given the probability that the event will happen

Key points

* You can **add** probabilities.
* The **sum** of the probabilities for all the possible outcomes is **1**.
* If the **probability** that an event will occur is **p**, then the probability it will **not** occur is **1 − p**.

Guided

1 A spinner has three coloured sections. The table shows the probability of landing on red or yellow.

Colour	Red	Yellow	Blue
Probability	0.25	0.45	

Hint
The spinner can only land on one colour. This means that the probabilities must add up to 1.

Find the probability that the spinner lands on blue.

....

Hint
You need to work out $1 - \frac{7}{11}$. It helps to write 1 as $\frac{11}{11}$

2 The probability that my team wins on Saturday is $\frac{7}{11}$.

The probability that my team does **not** win on Saturday is ....

3 The table shows the probabilities of scoring 1, 2, 3, 4 or 5 with a biased six-sided dice.

Score	1	2	3	4	5	6
Probability	0.1	0.1	0.2	0.3	0.2	

Remember this
A biased dice gives scores that are not equally likely.

a Find the probability of scoring 6.

Hint
The probabilities must add up to 1.

....

b Which score is most likely? ....

Hint
This will be the score with the highest probability.

c Find the probability of scoring 3 or 4. ....

Hint
Add the probabilities for the individual events.

d Find the probability of **not** scoring 1. ....

Practice

4 The probability that it will rain in my region today is 0.7
What is the probability that it will **not** rain in my region today? ....

5 Elaine chooses a crayon at random from her pencil case.
The probability that the crayon is purple is $\frac{2}{9}$ and the probability that it is red is $\frac{1}{9}$.
Find the probability that the crayon is:

Remember this
To add or subtract fractions with the same denominator, add or subtract the numerators.

a purple or red .... **b** **not** purple. ....

6 The table shows the probabilities that the Year 11 hockey team will win or lose their next match.

Result	Win	Lose	Draw
Probability	0.53	0.32	

Find the probability that the Year 11 hockey team will:

a draw their next match ....

b **not** lose their next match. ....

Step into GCSE

7 Angela has a box of chocolates. She takes a chocolate at random. The table shows the flavours and their probabilities of being selected.

Flavour	Toffee	Caramel	Raspberry	Truffle	Praline
Probability	0.2		0.3	0.1	0.15

a Find the probability that Angela selects a caramel. ....

b Find the probability that Angela doesn't select a praline. ....

Angela's favourite flavours are toffee and truffle.

c Find the probability that Angela selects one of her favourites. ....

Needs more practice ☐ Almost there ☐ I'm proficient! ☐

5.5 List outcomes

By the end of this section you will know how to:

* Systematically list all of the outcomes of a single event or two successive events

GCSE LINKS

AF: 26.4 Sample space diagrams; **BF:** Unit 1 5.5 Sample space diagrams; **16+:** 23.3 Record all possible outcomes of an event in a sample space diagram; **S:** 7.2 The meaning of probability

Key points

* The **sample space** for an experiment is a list of all possible outcomes.

Guided

1 The sample space for spinning a coin is Heads Tails

2 The sample space for rolling an ordinary six-sided dice is ....

Hint
List all of the outcomes for the dice.

3 Here is a spinner.

red, red, yellow, yellow, yellow

Hint
There are five outcomes for the spinner. Two outcomes are shown for you.

The sample space for the spinner is red red ....

Practice

4 Write down the sample space for this spinner.

green, green, green, blue, green, blue

....

5 One of the colours in the Union Jack is to be selected. Write down the sample space.

....

6 Write down the sample space for this spinner.

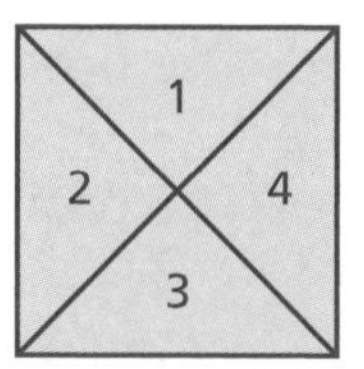

....

Guided

7 A coin and an ordinary six-sided dice are used in an experiment.
Write down the sample space. Use H for Head and T for Tails.

Hint
H1 means **H**eads on the coin and **1** on the dice

H1 H2 ....

Hint
There are two outcomes for the coin and six outcomes for the dice. This means that there are $2 \times 6 = 12$ outcomes in the sample space.

T1 T2 ....

8 Write down all of the possible outcomes for an experiment in which a coin is spun twice.

Hint
There are two outcomes for the first spin and two outcomes for the second spin, so there are $2 \times 2 = 4$ outcomes altogether.

HH ....

Practice

9 A car manufacturer offers three styles.

Saloon S
Estate E
Hatchback H

There are three colours available.

Black B
Red R
White W

You should know
For successive events the outcomes may be called **combinations**.

List all of the possible combinations of style and colour. The first two have been done for you.

SB SR ....

10 Here are six cards.
One white card and one black card are to be selected at random.
List all of the possible combinations.
The first two have been done for you.

Q W E R X Y

QX QY ....

GCSE

11 Sharon has two spinners.
She spins both spinners once.
List all of the possible outcomes.
One has been done for you.

Hint
Write the other outcomes using brackets and a comma in the same way.

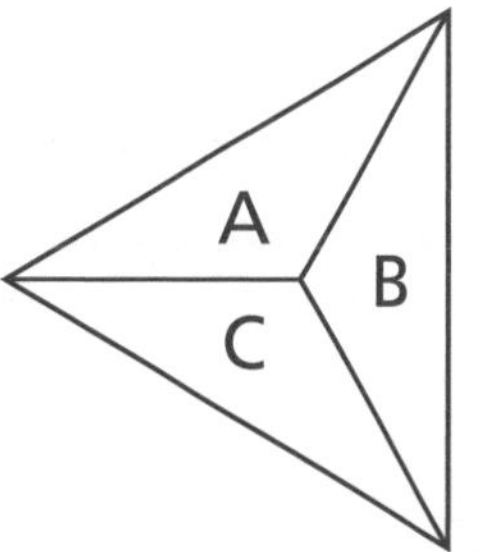

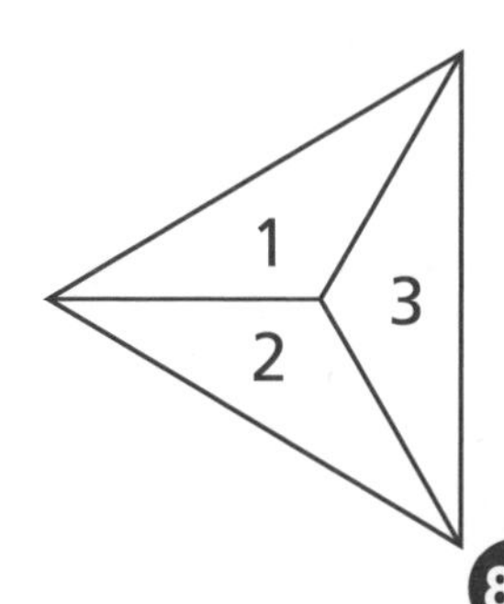

(A, 1) ....

....

Don't forget!

- In a probability experiment, the things that can happen are called ....
- The probability of an event that is **impossible** is ......
- The probability of any event must lie between ...... and ...... inclusive.
- When all of the possible outcomes are equally likely:

  Probability of an event $= \dfrac{\text{The number of outcomes in ....}}{\text{The total ....}}$

- In an experiment:

  Relative frequency of an event $= \dfrac{\text{The number of trials where the event occurred}}{\text{..........}}$

- The relative frequency becomes more reliable as an estimate of probability as the number of trials is ....
- Repeating an experiment will usually produce .... outcomes.
- The sum of the probabilities for all possible outcomes is ......
- The probability that an event will **not** occur is 1 – the probability that ....
- The .... for an experiment is the list of all possible outcomes.

Exam-style questions

1 A bag contains six blue pens, three green pens and one red pen.
A pen is selected at random.

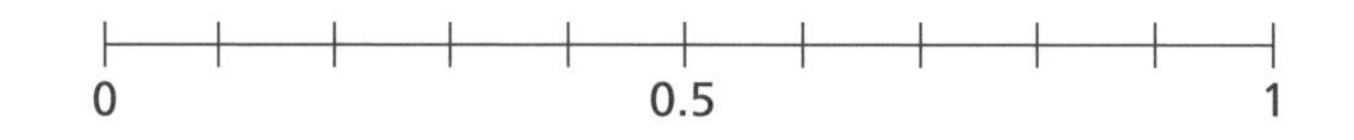

a Mark the point B on the scale to show the probability that the pen is blue.

b Mark the point R on the scale to show the probability that the pen is **not** red.

c Mark the point X on the scale to show the probability that the pen is blue, green or red.

2 The two-way table shows some information about the dogs in a rescue centre.

	Short straight hair	Long straight hair	Curly hair
Brown	5	3	1
Black	4	7	2
White	4	2	0

a How many dogs are there at the centre? ....

A dog is selected at random. Find the probability that the dog is:

b brown .... **c** **not** white ....

d black with long straight hair .... **e** white with curly hair. ....

3 Erica has some cards. Each card is either red or black.
She selects a card at random, then she records the colour and puts it back in the pack.
She does this 50 times.
The table shows her results.

Red	Black
35	15

a Estimate the probability that the next card selected at random will be red.

....

b Estimate the probability that the next card selected at random will be black.

....

4 The chef at a restaurant has recorded the dessert choices of the last 50 customers.

Apple pie	Cheese and biscuits	Crème brûlée	Sticky toffee pudding
16	7	15	

a Estimate the probability that a customer selected at random chooses sticky toffee pudding.

....

b Estimate the probability that a customer selected at random chooses apple pie or crème brûlée.

....

5 Andy is playing tennis. The table shows some probabilities based on his serve.
For each serve, there are only three possible outcomes.

Serves a fault	Serves in but not an ace	Serves an ace
25%	55%	

a What is the probability of Andy serving an ace?

....

b What is the probability that Andy either serves a fault or serves an ace?

....

6 James has organised some maths revision sessions.
Students choose one morning session and one afternoon session.
List all of the possible combinations.
The first one is done for you.

Morning	Solving equations Formulae Number	S F N
Afternoon	Representing data Geometry Probability	D G P

SD ....

....

Practice Paper

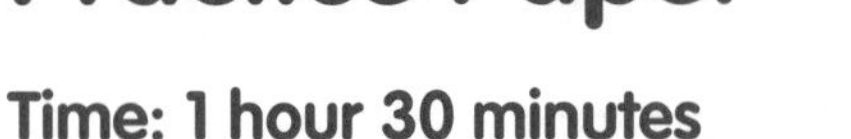

Time: 1 hour 30 minutes

Edexcel publishes Sample Assessment Material on its website. This Practice Exam Paper has been written to help you practise what you have learned and may not be representative of a real exam paper.

1 Helen owns a hair salon.
The pictogram shows the numbers of clients the salon had in one week.

Monday	
Tuesday	
Wednesday	
Thursday	
Friday	
Saturday	

Key: represents 8 people

a There were 36 clients on Wednesday.
Show this information on the pictogram. (1)

b How many clients were there altogether in the week?

....
(3)

(Total for Question 1 is 4 marks)

---

2 Students at The Manor School are assessed in maths.
Each student is awarded a Level.
The table shows this information.

	Level achieved				
Year group	**4**	**5**	**6**	**7**	**8**
7	43	116	28	0	0
8	31	72	63	22	0
9	14	31	85	32	18
Total					

a Complete the table. (2)

b How many students achieved Level 5?

....
(1)

c How many Year 8 students achieved Level 6 or higher?

....
(2)

(Total for Question 2 is 5 marks)

---

3 Here are some events.

A A coin is spun and shows Heads.

B An ordinary dice is rolled and lands on 5.

C A red card is selected at random from five red cards and one black card.

Show the probability of each event by writing A, B and C in their correct positions on this probability scale.

0 ———————— $\frac{1}{2}$ ———————— 1

(Total for Question 3 is 3 marks)

4 Mike is an office manager. He wants to know how many letters are sent from his office each day. Design a suitable data collection sheet. Allow for up to 30 letters each day.

(Total for Question 4 is 4 marks)

---

5 In a school talent contest, each member of the audience voted for their favourite performer. The bar chart shows the results.

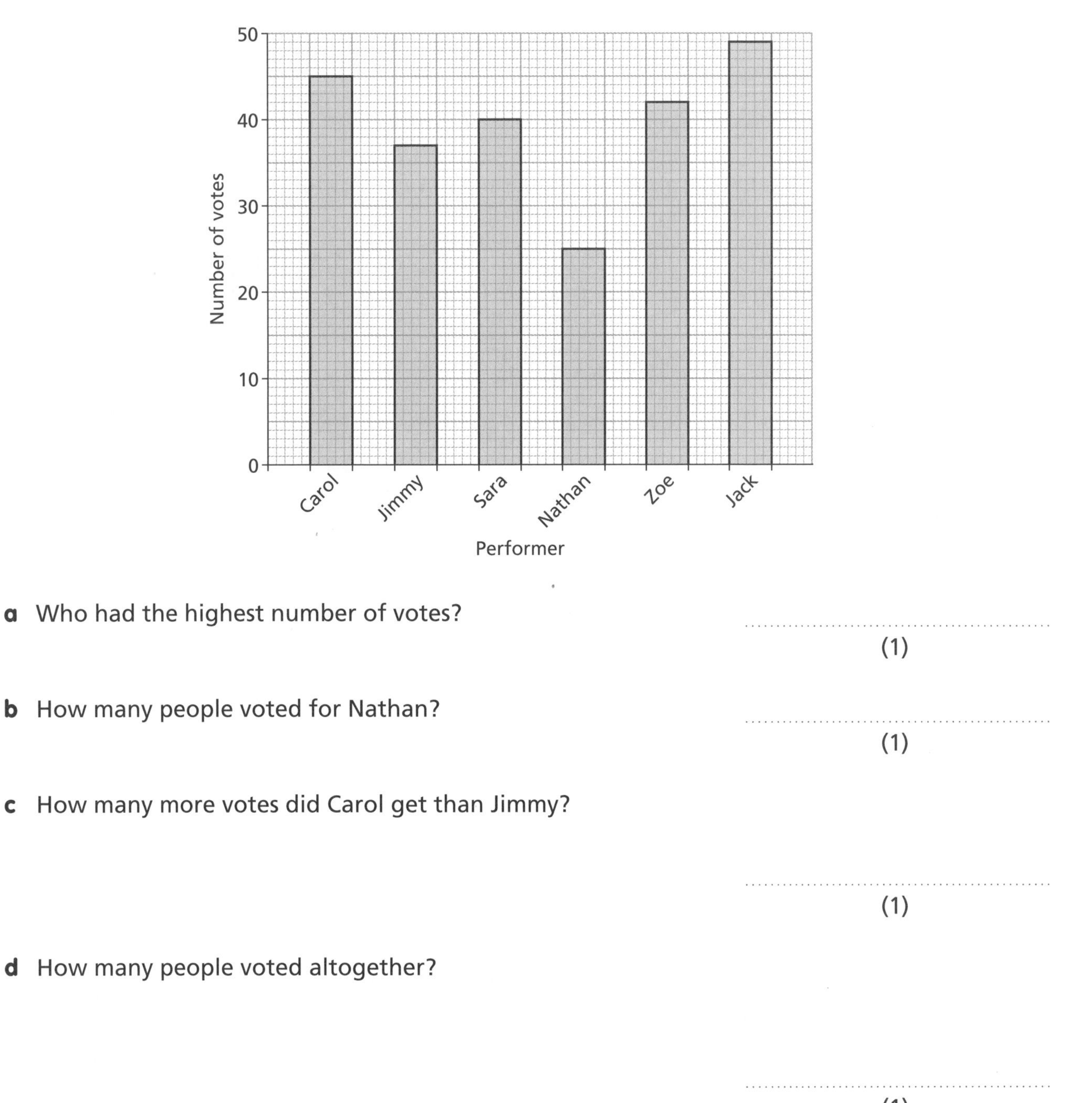

a Who had the highest number of votes? .... (1)

b How many people voted for Nathan? .... (1)

c How many more votes did Carol get than Jimmy?

.... (1)

d How many people voted altogether?

.... (1)

(Total for Question 5 is 4 marks)

6 Here are the amounts of weight, in kilograms, lost by 10 dieters in two weeks.

1 5 3 1 2 0 1 4 3 2

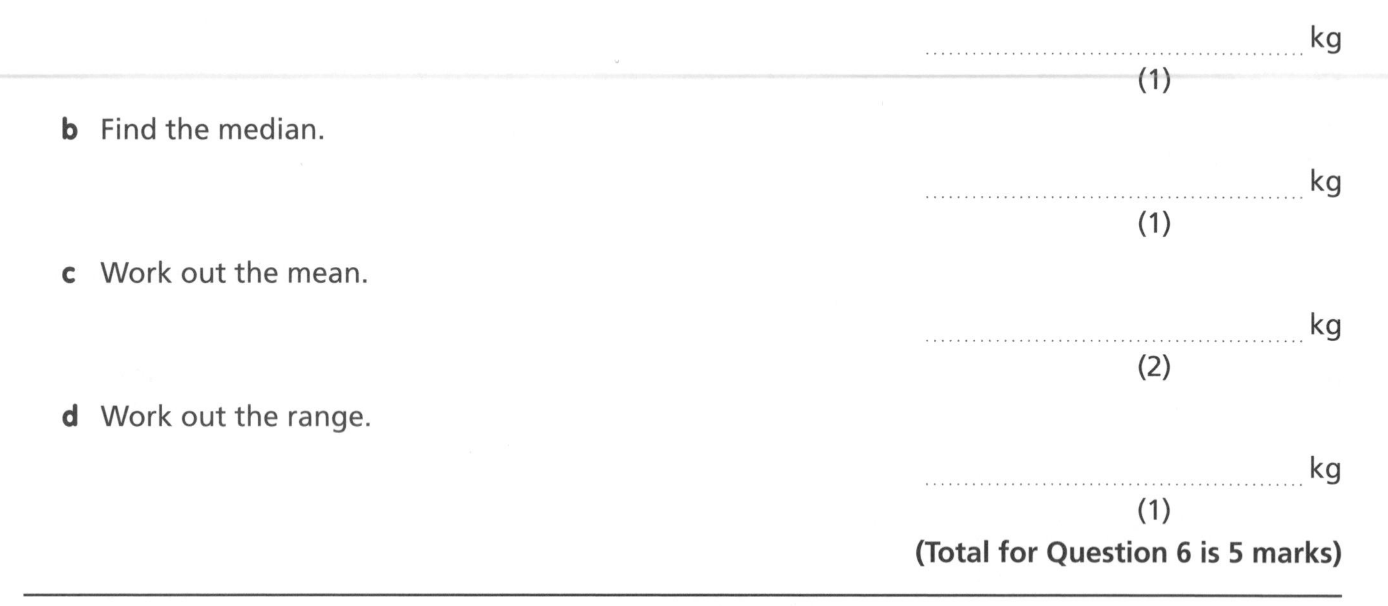

a Write down the mode.

.... kg

(1)

b Find the median.

.... kg

(1)

c Work out the mean.

.... kg

(2)

d Work out the range.

.... kg

(1)

(Total for Question 6 is 5 marks)

---

7 The temperature of the Earth's atmosphere was measured at different heights.
The results are given in the table.

Height (km)	0	0.2	0.4	0.6	0.8	1.0	1.2	1.4	1.6	1.8	2.0
Temperature (°C)	20	18	17	15	14	11	9	6	4	2	0

a Draw a scatter graph to show this information.

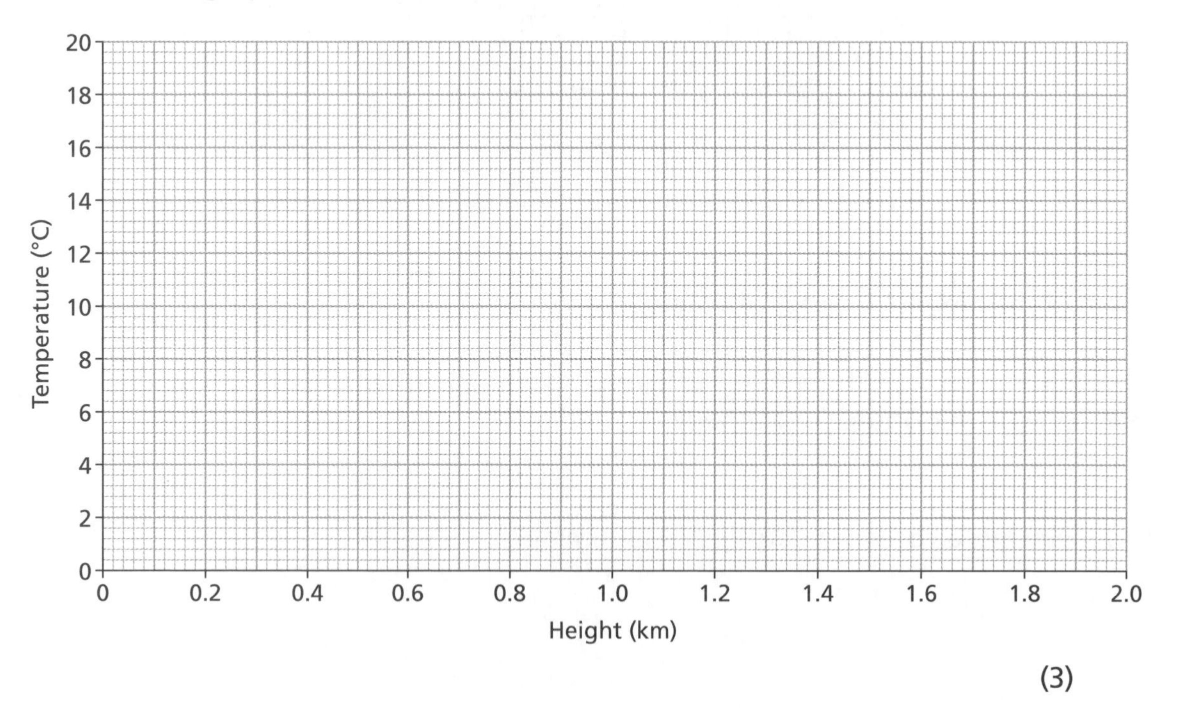

(3)

b Describe the correlation between the temperature of the atmosphere and the height.

....

....

(2)

(Total for Question 7 is 5 marks)

8 James has 20 red cards and 10 black cards.
He takes one of the cards at random.
Find the probability that the card will be a red card.

....

(Total for Question 8 is 3 marks)

---

9 A new housing development has three types of property:

D detached
S semi-detached
T terraced

Each type of property may have one of the following:

G garage
P car port
C conservatory

List all of the possible combinations. The first two are done for you.

DG DP ....

....

(Total for Question 9 is 2 marks)

---

10 A biased spinner can land on one of four colours.
The table shows the probability for each colour.

Colour	Blue	Green	Red	Yellow
Probability	0.3	0.1		0.4

The spinner is spun once. Find the probability that:

a it will land on Red

....
(2)

b it will land on Blue or Yellow

....
(1)

c it will **not** land on Green.

....
(1)

(Total for Question 10 is 4 marks)

---

11 In a survey students were asked about their favourite pets.
The dual bar chart shows the results.

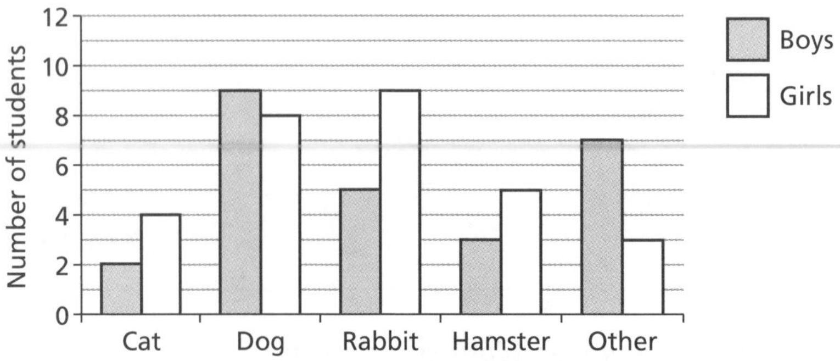

Number of students
12
10
8
6
4
2
0
Cat Dog Rabbit Hamster Other
Boys
Girls

a Which pet did more boys choose than any other? ....

(1)

b How many girls chose hamster? ....

(1)

c How many more girls than boys chose cat? ....

(1)

d Which pet was chosen by the greatest total number of students?

....

(1)

(Total for Question 11 is 4 marks)

---

12 Jemal is conducting a survey about competition dancing.
He asks some dancers this question.

How many hours do you spend practising?

5–10 10–15 15–20 More than 20

Write down three things wrong with this question.

1 ....

2 ....

3 ....

(Total for Question 12 is 3 marks)

13 Some students sold raffle tickets for Red Nose Day.
The stem and leaf diagram shows information about the number of tickets each of them sold.

1	2	6	7			
2	1	4	4	8		
3	2	2	2	5	7	9
4	3	4	4	6	8	
5	4	6				
6	3					

Key: 2 | 4 represents 24

a Find the mode of the number of tickets sold.

....
(1)

b How many students sold more than 40 tickets?

....
(1)

c Find the range.

....
(1)

(Total for Question 13 is 3 marks)

---

14 The table shows some of the winning times, in seconds, for the men's 100 m sprint in Olympic finals.

Year	1980	1984	1988	1992	1996	2000	2004	2008	2012
Time (s)	10.25	9.99	9.92	9.96		9.87	9.85		9.63

The results are shown on this time-series graph.

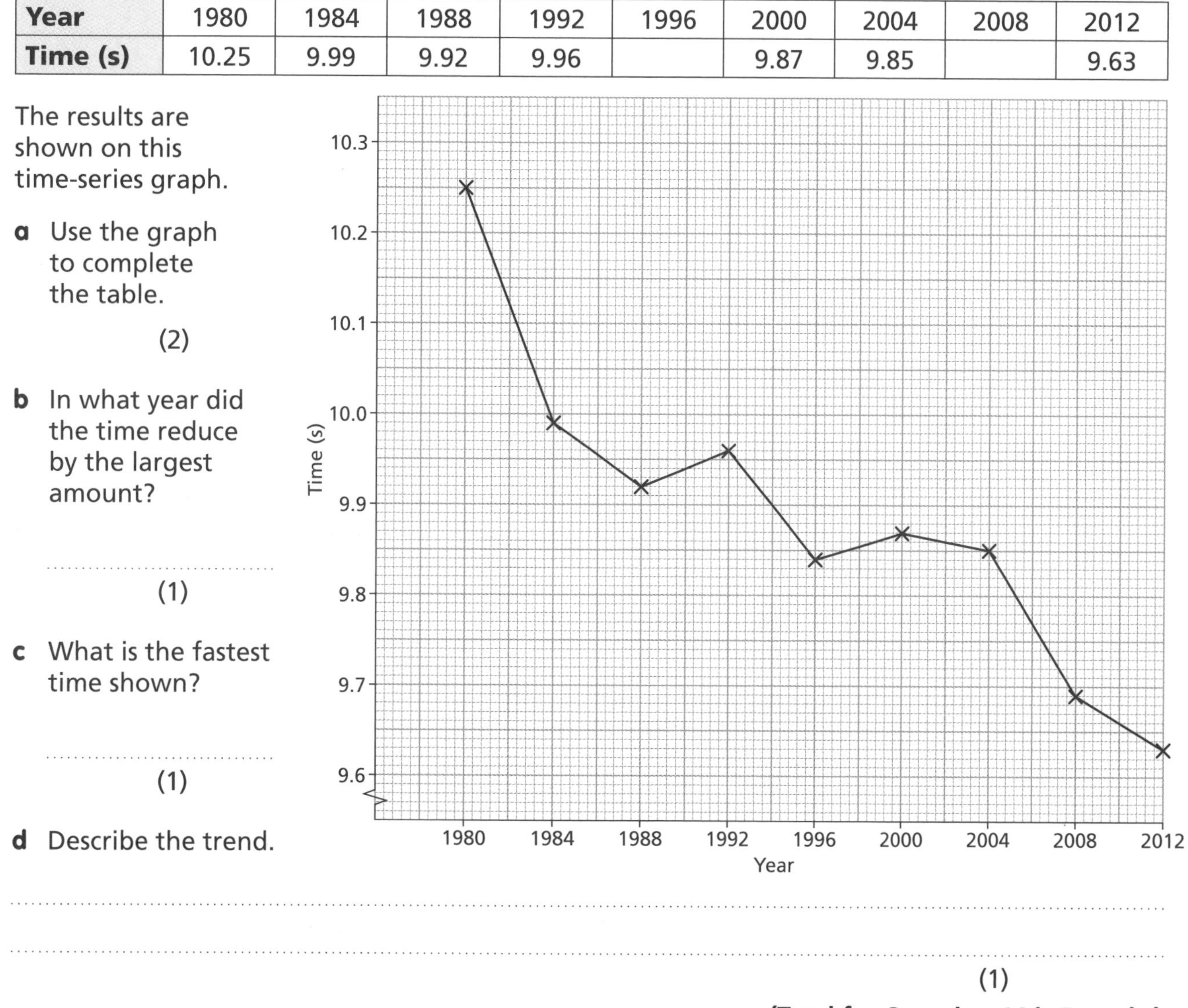

a Use the graph to complete the table.

(2)

b In what year did the time reduce by the largest amount?

....
(1)

c What is the fastest time shown?

....
(1)

d Describe the trend.

....

....
(1)

(Total for Question 14 is 5 marks)

15 Jake has a biased coin.
He wants to estimate the probability that the coin will land on Heads.
Jake spins the coin 10 times. The coin lands on Heads 4 times.

a Write down an estimate for the probability that the next time Jake spins the coin it will land on Heads.

....

(1)

b Comment on the reliability of Jake's estimate.

....

....

....

(1)

(Total for Question 15 is 2 marks)

---

16 Dan is a cricketer.
Here are the numbers of runs he scored in each of the last 10 matches.

15 28 45 24 36 57 25 18 3 48

Rob is also a cricketer. He plays for the same team.
His mean score is 29.5 and his range is 26.

Compare the performances of the two players.

....

....

....

....

....

....

(Total for Question 16 is 3 marks)

---

17 The bar chart shows the numbers of singles downloaded between 2010 and 2013.

Give three reasons why this chart may be misleading.

1 ....

....

2 ....

....

3 ....

....

(Total for Question 17 is 3 marks)

18 A small hotel has three floors.
There are three types of room available on each floor.
The two-way table gives information about where the guests stayed one night.

		Type of room			
		Single	**Twin**	**Double**	**Total**
Floor	**3**		8	12	23
	2	2	6		
	1	1		16	
	Total		22		66

a Complete the two-way table.

(2)

A guest is chosen at random.

b Find the probability that the guest has a double room on the second floor.

....

(2)

(Total for Question 18 is 4 marks)

---

19 Vicky has 45 apps on her mobile phone.
The table shows how many she has in each category.

Productivity	Entertainment	Health and fitness	Games
8	10	5	22

Draw a pie chart for this information.

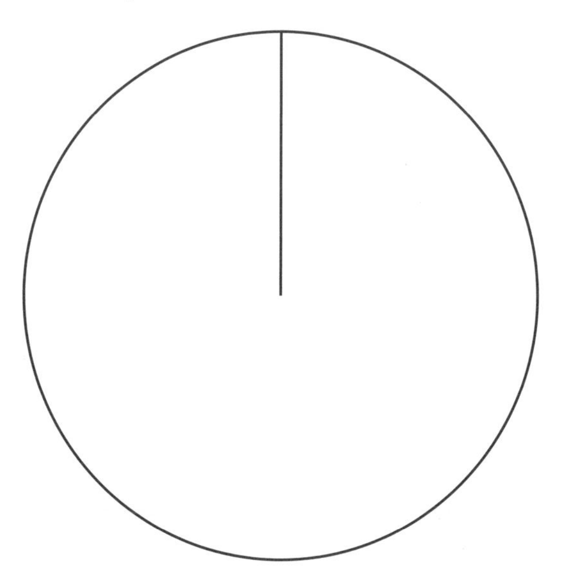

(Total for Question 19 is 4 marks)

20 Jess recorded the lengths of 30 Timber Rattlesnakes.
Here are her results in metres.

1.36	1.27	0.96	1.21	1.05	1.16	1.04	0.98	1.24	1.11
1.18	1.02	1.33	1.24	1.18	1.30	1.12	1.26	0.92	1.00
1.24	1.16	1.12	1.39	1.10	1.27	1.06	1.09	1.28	1.25

Complete the grouped frequency table for the data.

Length (l m)	Tally	Frequency
$0.90 < l \leqslant 1.00$		
$1.00 < l \leqslant 1.10$		
$1.10 < l \leqslant 1.20$		
$1.20 < l \leqslant 1.30$		
$1.30 < l \leqslant 1.40$		

(Total for Question 20 is 3 marks)

---

21 The table shows the numbers of children in 30 households.

Number of children	Frequency
0	0
1	10
2	12
3	6
4	

No household had more than four children.

Work out the total number of children in these households.

....

(Total for Question 21 is 3 marks)

22 Toby did a survey to find out which type of device people used most often to access the internet. The pie chart shows this information.

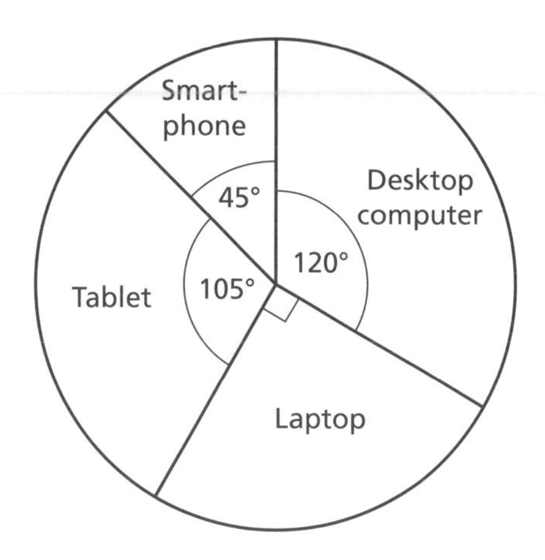

a Which device did most people choose?

....
(1)

Three people chose Smartphone.

b How many chose Tablet?

....
(1)

c How many people were included in the survey?

....
(2)

(Total for Question 22 is 4 marks)

TOTAL FOR PAPER IS 80 MARKS

Answers

1 Data

1.1 Types of data

1 The colour of a car → categorical
The weight of an apple → continuous
The number of people who vote in an election → discrete
The number of pages in a book → discrete

2 a Categorical **b** Discrete **c** Categorical

3 a Categorical **b** Discrete

4 Type of butterfly – categorical. Wingspan – Continuous

5 a Discrete **b** Categorical

6

	Data type		
Data	**Categorical**	**Discrete**	**Continuous**
The temperature inside an oven			✓
The number of sweets in a jar		✓	
The time taken to toast some bread			✓
The colour of a tin of paint	✓		
The number of days in a month		✓	

1.2 Data collection

1 a

Number rolled	Tally	Frequency
1	卌卌	10
2	卌IIII	9
3	卌卌I	11
4	卌IIII	9
5	卌卌I	11
6	卌卌	10

b Total = 60

c The expected total is 60 since the dice was rolled 60 times.

2 a

Guess	Tally	Frequency
301–330	III	3
331–360	III	3
361–390	卌卌卌I	16
391–420	卌III	8
421–450	卌卌I	11
451–480	卌	5

b 46

3

Height (h m)	Tally	Frequency
$1.60 < h \leqslant 1.65$	III	3
$1.65 < h \leqslant 1.70$	IIII	4
$1.70 < h \leqslant 1.75$	卌	5
$1.75 < h \leqslant 1.80$	卌	5
$1.80 < h \leqslant 1.85$	卌I	6
$1.85 < h \leqslant 1.90$	IIII	4
$1.90 < h \leqslant 1.95$	III	3

4 a

Number spun	Tally	Frequency
1	卌II	7
2	卌卌	10
3	卌II	7
4	卌III	8
5	卌III	8

b 2

5

Number of texts	Tally	Frequency
11–40	卌II	7
41– 80	卌I	6
81–110	卌III	8
111–150	IIII	4
151–200	卌	5

b It is sensible to group the data because the values are so varied.

c 5

6

Length (l cm)	Tally	Frequency
$12.0 < l \leqslant 13.0$	III	3
$13.0 < l \leqslant 14.0$	II	2
$14.0 < l \leqslant 15.0$	IIII	4
$15.0 < l \leqslant 16.0$	II	2
$16.0 < l \leqslant 17.0$	卌	5
$17.0 < l \leqslant 18.0$	IIII	4
$18.0 < l \leqslant 19.0$	卌	5
$19.0 < l \leqslant 20.0$	卌	5

7

Number of goals	Tally	Frequency
0	卌II	7
1	卌卌	10
2	卌卌II	12
3	卌	5
4	IIII	4
5	I	1
6	I	1

8 a

Programme	Tally	Frequency
American Idol		
Bear Grylls		
Coronation Street		
EastEnders		
Master Chef		
Modern Family		
QI		
The Love Machine		
The X Factor		

b Categorical

9 a

Shoe size	Tally	Frequency
$5–5\frac{1}{2}$	III	3
$6–6\frac{1}{2}$	卌I	6
$7–7\frac{1}{2}$	III	3
$8–8\frac{1}{2}$	III	3
$9–9\frac{1}{2}$	卌	5
$10–10\frac{1}{2}$	IIII	4
$11–11\frac{1}{2}$	II	2

b Discrete

1.3 Criticise questionnaires

1 a The question is heavily biased by suggesting what the expected answer is.
b The amounts are very high: this may embarrass people who earn a lot less.
c There is no clear distinction between Quite often, Sometimes and Not very often.
d The categories overlap. It is not clear which box to tick for 5 or 10 books.

2 a The question is biased by referring to the 'beautiful' countryside.
b There is no option for people who don't eat meat.
c The categories overlap: it is not clear which box to tick for 1, 2 or 3 hours.
d The question assumes that there is something wrong with the new lunch menu.
e The question is too difficult: most people won't be able to recall details with accuracy over such a long time.
f Use of the words 'Do you agree' suggests what the expected response is.

3 a disagree; disagree
b prefer
c 7–9 hours; 9 hours
d Don't know

4 a If someone wants to choose 6 hours then it isn't clear which box they should tick.
b The intervals are not very wide – most people won't know the answer with sufficient accuracy to answer the question.
c Use of the words 'Do you agree' suggests the expected response.

5 a How tall are you?
☐ Less than 1.5 m ☐ 1.5 m–less than 1.7 m
☐ 1.7 m–1.8 m ☐ More than 1.8 m
b How do you feel about the proposal that the school has a new navy blue uniform?
☐ Strongly agree ☐ Agree ☐ Disagree
☐ Strongly disagree ☐ Don't know

6 a Use of the words 'Do you agree' suggests the expected response.
b Should Scotland be an independent country?
☐ Yes ☐ No

1.4 Reliability

1 Answer should include: bias in the sample of people due to the choice of location and time; the sample is likely to include those people most inconvenienced by the proposed change.

2 Answer should include: Year 7 pupils are quite likely to want to please their English teacher; top set pupils experience most success in the subject; the sample is biased in favour of English.

3 Answer should include: people who work in the same office are likely to influence each other; a sample of 10 people is too small to represent the full range of opinions.

4 Answer should include: bias is introduced through the timing of the survey; people who are at work will be largely excluded; the views are unlikely to represent the general population of the town.

5 Answer should include: selecting people at random is good but the sample is already biased because all of the people are from the same area; it is unlikely that the sample will fairly represent the views of people from across all areas of the town.

6 a Answer should include: the choice of time and location introduces bias into the sample; many football supporters are likely to be included; the results are likely to unfairly favour football.
b Answer should include: change the day and the timing of the survey; take the views of males and females of different ages; possibly combine the results from different locations and different times to eliminate bias.

Don't forget!

* specific
* numerical, range
* words, numbers
* grouped, class
* questions, a particular purpose
* response
* accurately represents
* random sample

Exam-style questions

1 a

Vehicle	Tally	Frequency
Bus	II	2
Car	卌卌卌卌卌II	27
Motorbike	II	2
Truck	卌IIII	9
Van	卌卌	10

b Categorical

2 Should Year 11 students always be in the first sitting for lunch?
☐ Yes ☐ No ☐ Don't know

3 Answer should include the following points in any order:
1 Allowance is not made for people who don't read magazines or who read more than 4 magazines.
2 It isn't clear which box to tick for 2 or for 3 magazines.
3 The question doesn't specify the time period for the magazines to be read.

2 Displaying data

2.1 Pictograms

1 **Pictogram showing people attending the school production**

Monday	☺☺☺☺☺☺☺☺☺☺☺☺
Tuesday	☺☺☺☺☺☺☺☺☺
Wednesday	☺☺☺☺☺☺☺☺☺☺
Thursday	☺☺☺☺☺☺☺☺
Friday	☺☺☺☺☺☺☺☺☺☺☺☺☺
Saturday	☺☺☺☺☺☺☺☺☺☺☺☺☺☺☺

Key: ☺ represents 10 people

2 b **c** **d**

3

Time	Number of customers
7 pm	⊕⊕⊕⊕⊕⊕
8 pm	⊕⊕⊕⊕⊕⊕⊕⊕⊕ (part)
9 pm	⊕⊕⊕⊕⊕⊕⊕⊕⊕⊕⊕ (part)
10 pm	⊕⊕⊕⊕⊕⊕⊕⊕
11 pm	⊕⊕⊕⊕⊕⊕ (part)

4

Day	Number of letters received
Monday	▭▭▭▭▭▭▭▭ (part)
Tuesday	▭▭▭▭▭▭
Wednesday	▭▭▭▭▭▭▭ (part)
Thursday	▭▭▭▭▭ (part)
Friday	▭▭▭▭▭▭▭

Key: ▭ represents 2 letters

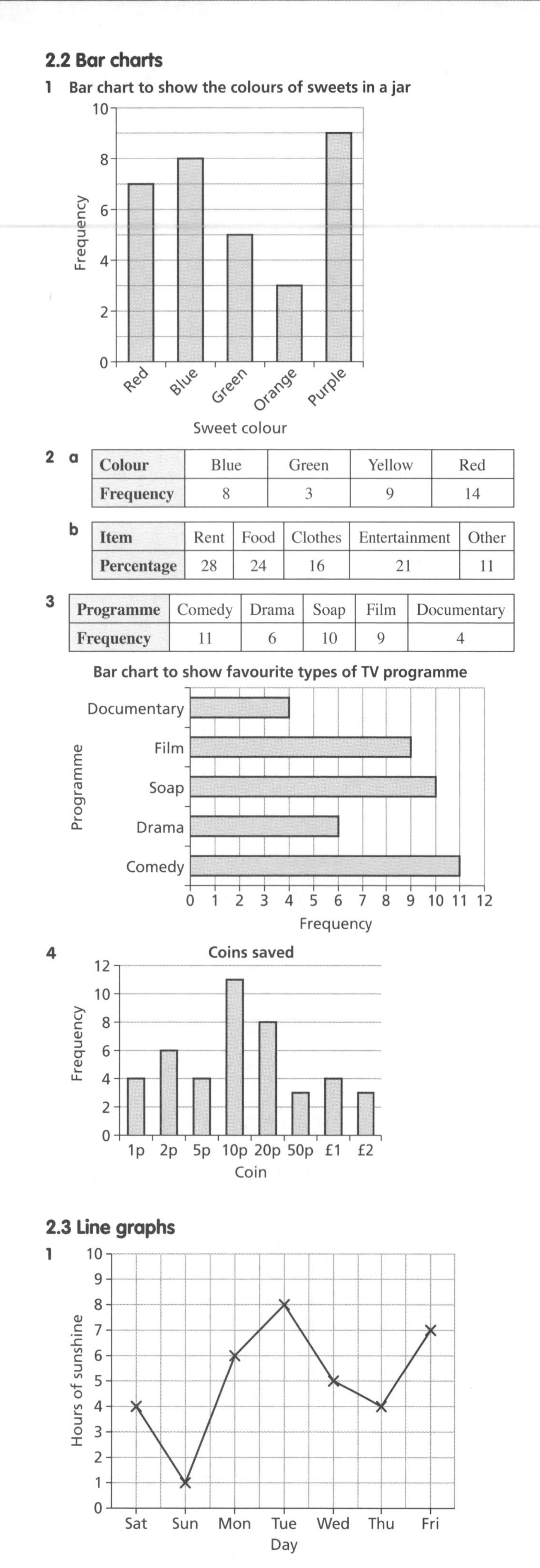

2.2 Bar charts

1 Bar chart to show the colours of sweets in a jar

2 a

Colour	Blue	Green	Yellow	Red
Frequency	8	3	9	14

b

Item	Rent	Food	Clothes	Entertainment	Other
Percentage	28	24	16	21	11

3

Programme	Comedy	Drama	Soap	Film	Documentary
Frequency	11	6	10	9	4

Bar chart to show favourite types of TV programme

4 Coins saved

2.3 Line graphs

1

2

3

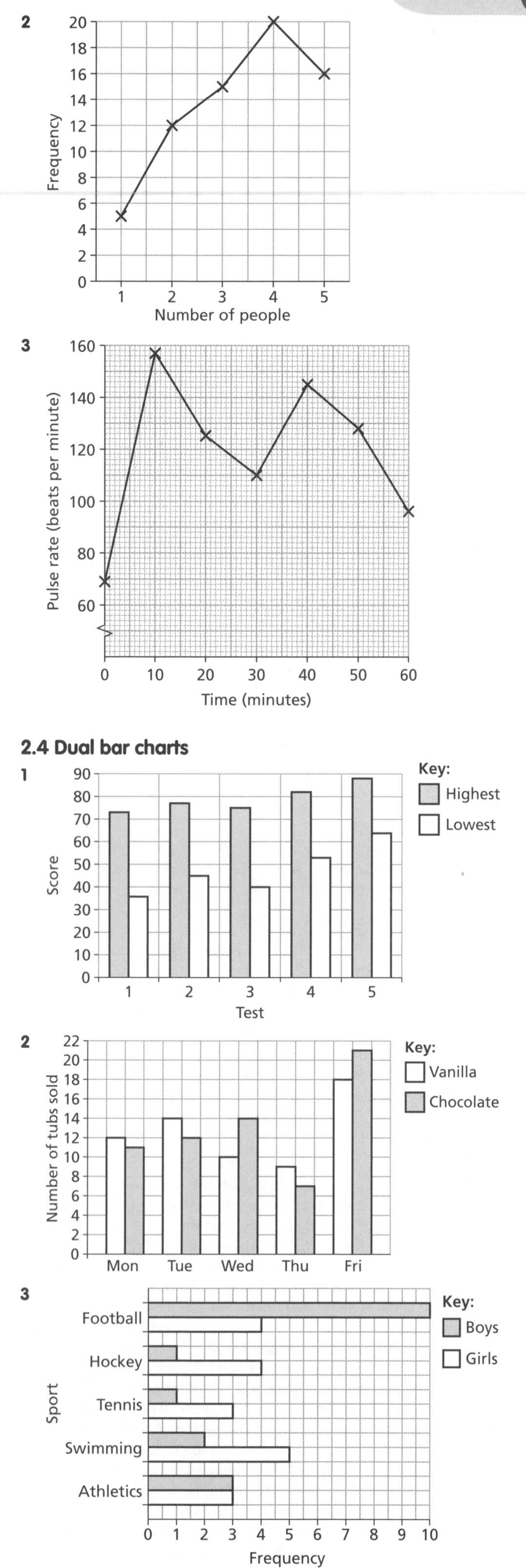

2.4 Dual bar charts

1

2

3

4

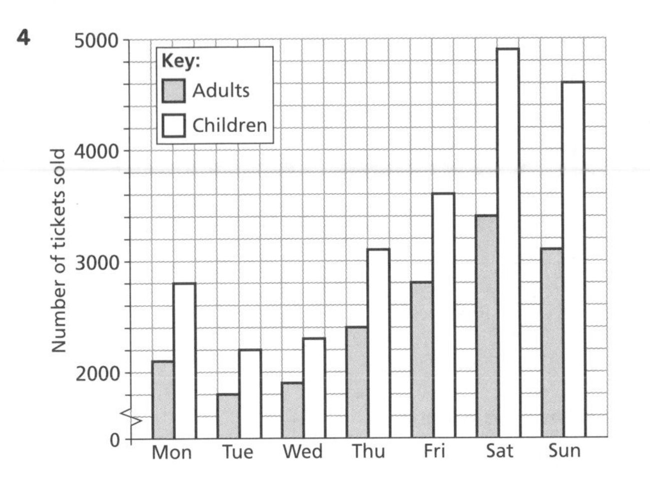

2.5 Two-way tables

1

	Art	Biol	Chem	Econ	Eng	Geog	Hist	Maths	Phys	Total
Boys	1	3	1	2	3	3	3	4	2	22
Girls	3	4	1	1	3	1	3	4	0	20
Total	4	7	2	3	6	4	6	8	2	42

2

	French	German	Spanish	Total
Boys	7	6	5	18
Girls	8	7	9	24
Total	15	13	14	42

3

	Cat	Dog	Fish	Hamster	Mouse	Rabbit	Rat	Total
Boys	3	7	3	2	2	2	2	21
Girls	4	5	1	3	4	4	0	21
Total	7	12	4	5	6	6	2	42

4

	Sixth form	College	Work	Total
Boys	24	23	11	58
Girls	28	29	16	73
Total	52	52	27	131

5

	Did homework	Did not do homework	Total
Did bring equipment	24	2	26
Did not bring equipment	1	4	5
Total	25	6	31

2.6 Pie charts

1

Method of travel	Number of students	Angle of pie chart
Bus	14	$12° \times 14 = 168°$
Car	5	$12° \times 5 = 60°$
Cycle	3	$12° \times 3 = 36°$
Walk	8	$12° \times 8 = 96°$
Total	30	$12° \times 30 = 360°$

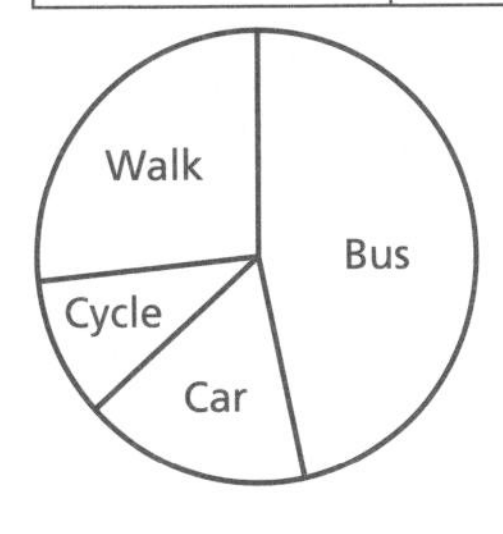

2

Fuel type	Number of vehicles	Angle of pie chart
Petrol	72	216°
Diesel	31	93°
Dual fuel	2	6°
Hybrid	15	45°
Total	120	360°

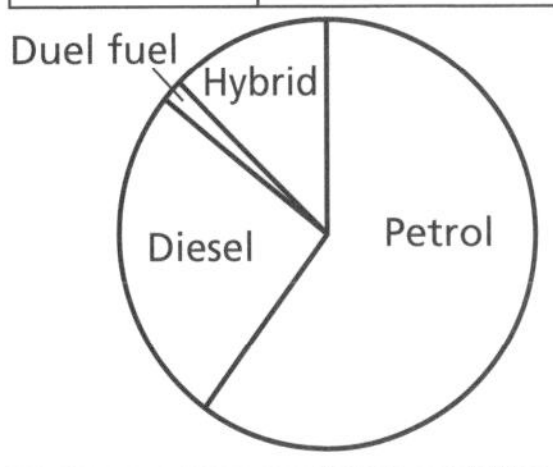

3

Waste type	Number of containers	Angle of pie chart
General waste	30	150°
Metal	8	40°
Organic	16	80°
Paper	6	30°
Wood	12	60°
Total	72	360°

4

Activity	Number of hours	Angle of pie chart
Sleeping	9	135°
Working	7	105°
Dining	2	30°
Relaxing	6	90°
Total	24	360°

2.7 Time-series graphs

1

2

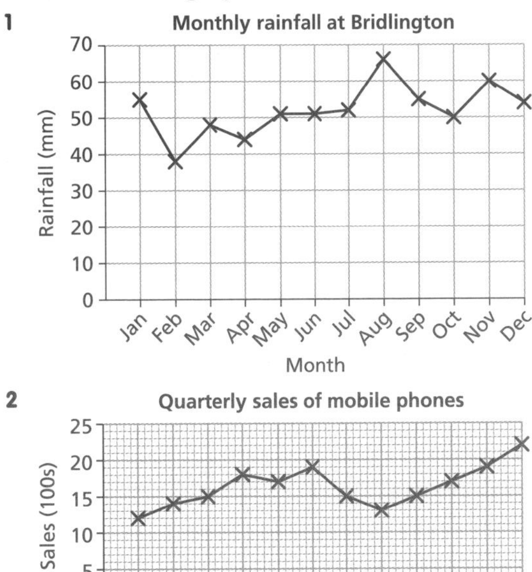

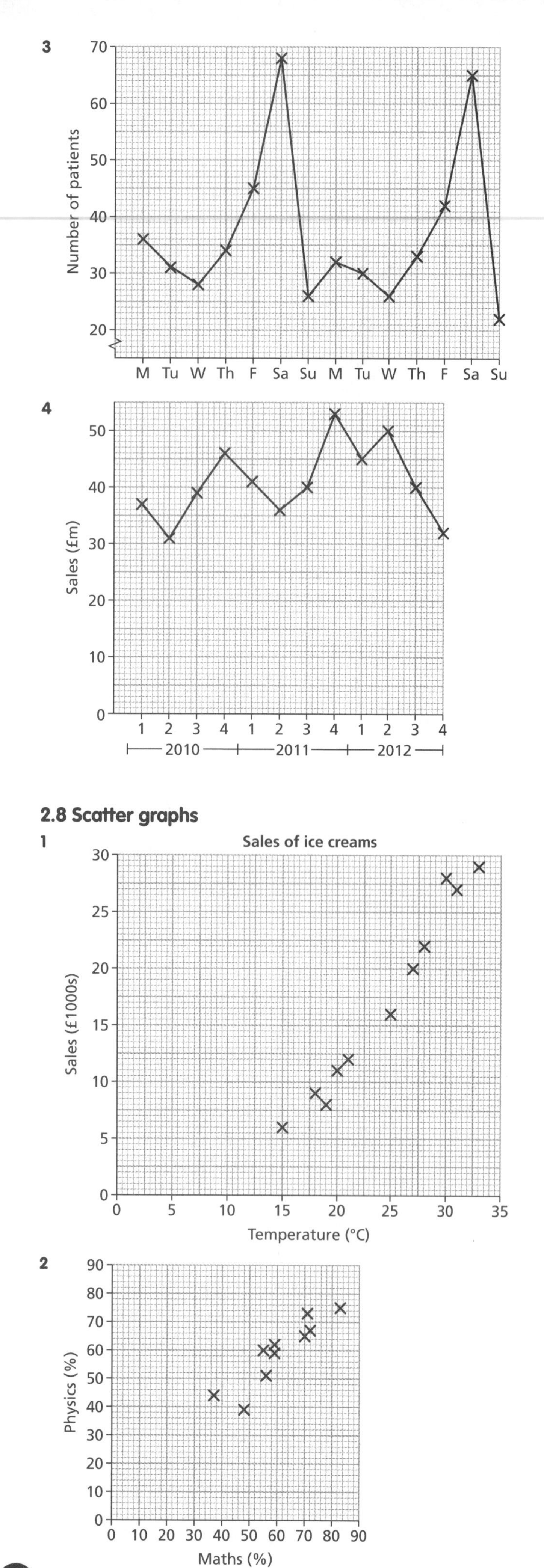

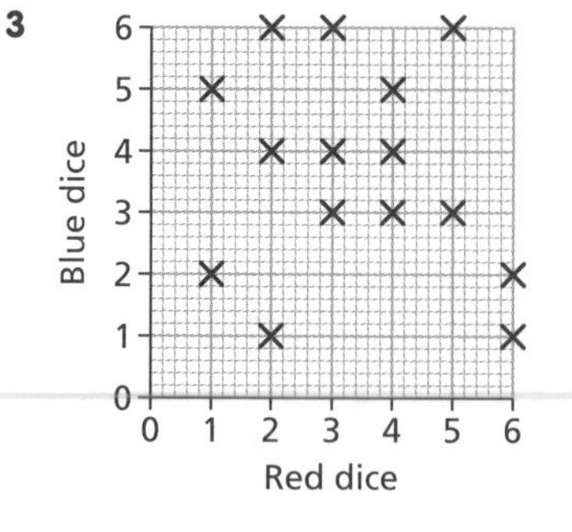

2.9 Misleading diagrams

1 1 There is no horizontal scale.
2 There are numbers on the vertical axis, but no units.

2 Answer should include the following: it is not a fair representation; the vertical scale doesn't start from 0; the effect is to make the increase in profits seem to be more significant.

3 Answer should include: the comparison is not fair; the symbols used for Type C are larger than those used for Type A and Type B; the effect is to make Type C look better than it is.

4 1 The circles exaggerate the visual impact of the difference in the scores.
2 The vertical scale isn't uniform – this makes the scores this season look better.

5 1 The line is too thick.
2 The vertical scale is not uniform.

6 1 The 3D effect makes it difficult to compare the sections of the pie chart.
2 The removal of the red sector makes the blue and yellow sectors look bigger as their edges can be seen.

Don't forget!

* key
* gap
* discrete
* comparisons
* total, columns
* small
* time
* scatter

Exam-style questions

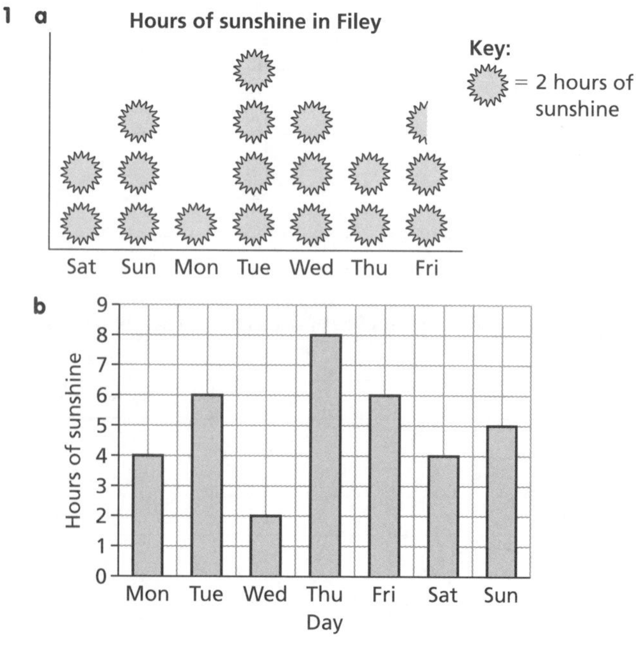

2

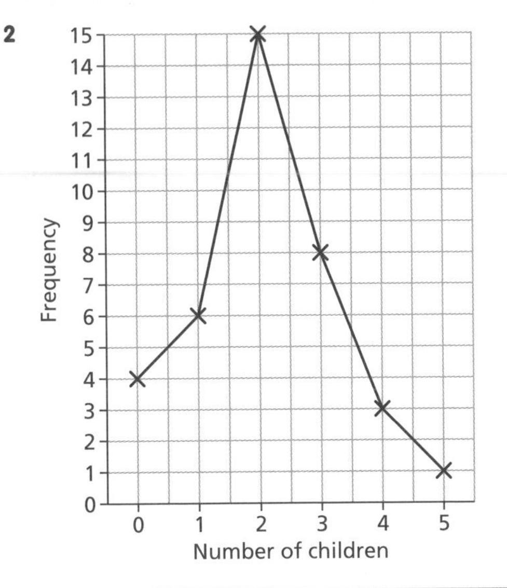

3

	Junior	Adult	Senior	Total
Standard	36	16	5	57
Full	5	18	10	33
Premium	0	25	0	25
Total	41	59	15	115

4

5

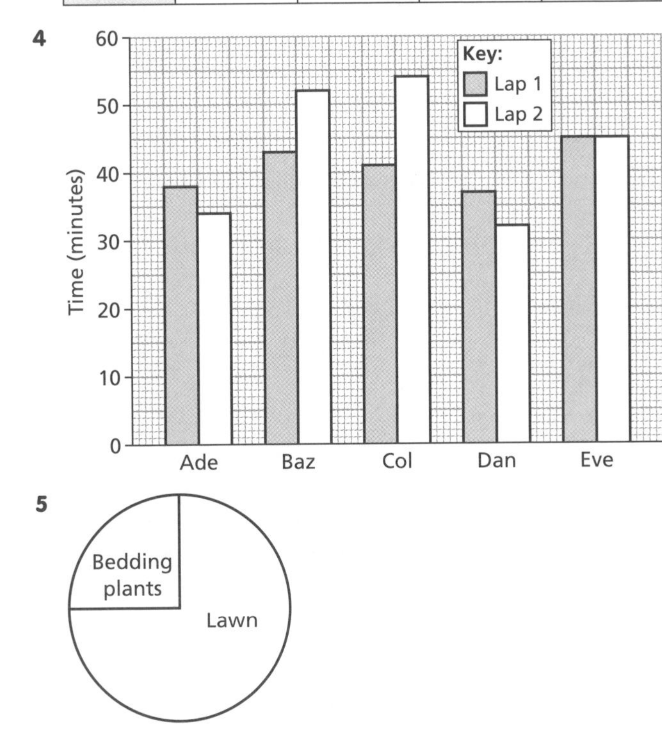

6

Book category	Number of books	Angle of pie chart
Comedy	12	96°
Thriller	7	56°
Mystery	9	72°
Romance	17	136°

7

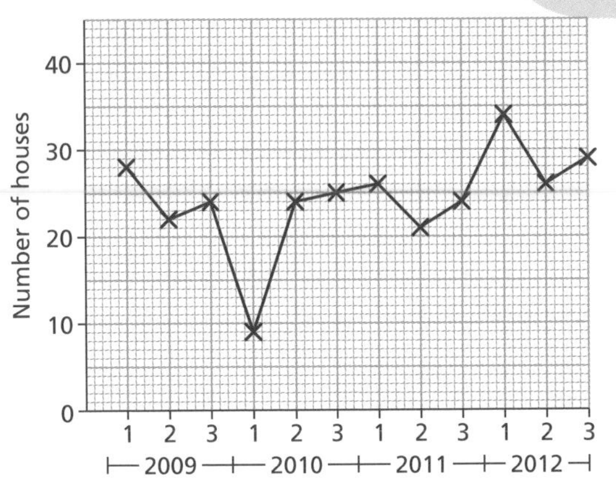

3 Calculating with data

3.1 Averages and range

1 white
2 1
3 4
4 3
5 48
6 blue
7 9, 11, 12, 15, 16, 16, 17, 18, 18. The median is 16
8 7, 7, 8, 8, 9, 9, 10, 10.
The numbers in the middle are 8 and 9. The median is 8.5
9 Median height = 180 cm
10 Median number of eggs = 8
11 Median number of press-ups = 21
12 Median cooking time = 15.5 minutes
13 Total = 3 + 0 + 2 + 1 + 5 + 2 + 1 + 2 = 16.
Mean = 16 ÷ 8 = 2
14 Total = 3 + 5 + 1 + 7 + 4 + 10 = 30. Mean = 30 ÷ 6 = 5
15 Mean = 5
16 Mean = 12
17 Mean = 24
18 Mean = 3.6
19 Largest salary = £1105. Smallest salary = £824.
Range = £1105 − £824 = £281
20 Range = 59
21 Range = 3.5 m
22 Range = 56 minutes
23 Range = 57 seconds
24 Range = 12°C

3.2 Range and mode from a stem and leaf diagram

1

1	1 2 5 6
2	2 3 7 7 8
3	1 4 6
4	0 2 3 9

Key: 2 | 3 means 23

2 Mode = 27
3 Largest number = 78. Smallest number = 34
Range = 78 − 34 = 44
4 a Mode = 65 beats per minute
b Range = 32 beats per minute
5 a Range = 47
b Mode = 53
6 a

2	9 9
3	0 1 4 7 7 8
4	3 4 5 6 8 8 9 9
5	0 3 4 7 7 7 8
6	3 4 6

Key: 4 | 3 = 43 miles per hour

b Mode = 57 miles per hour
c Range = 37 miles per hour
7 a Mode = £420
b Range = £370

Don't forget!

* average
* most often
* order
* total of all the data values, number of values
* range
* ordered
* mode

Exam-style questions

1 a Mode = 1
  b Median = 2
  c Mean = 2.27 to 3 sf
2 a Mean = 59
  b Median = 58
  c Range = 24
3 a Mode = 23 seconds
  b Median = 23 seconds
  c Mean = 23 seconds
4 a Mode = 158 rainy days
  b Range = 42 rainy days
5 a Mode = 34 miles
  b Range = 42 miles

4 Interpreting data

4.1 Read and interpret data from tables

1 a 124
  b Year 9
  c 124 + 116 = 240
2 a 1320 − 3 = 1303
  b 1317
3 a 547
  b 1883
  c 1254
4 a 113 miles
  b York
  c 122 + 113 = 235 miles
5 a −2°C
  b Cardiff
  c 4°C
6 a 0653
  b 22 minutes
7 a 3
  b 16
  c Jinty
  d 4
8 a 64 miles
  b Worcester
  c Sheffield
  d 298 miles
  e 49 miles
9 a 4
  b 2000
  c 4
  d 46
10 a Rum and raisin
  b 142
  c July
  d 558 litres
  e 139 litres

4.2 Interpret charts and graphs

1 a 45
  b Saturday
  c 15
  d 235
2 a 250 000 tonnes
  b 200 000 tonnes
  c 75 000 tonnes
3 a 3 million
  b British Museum
  c 500 000 or 0.5 million
  d 24 500 000 or 24.5 million
4 a Rottweiler
  b 7 years
  c 8.5 years
  d Bulldog
5 a Toyota Prius
  b Ferrari 458
6 a £60 000 000 or £60 million
  b 2009
  c 2011
7 a 4
  b Level 6
  c 20
  d 31
8 a 5
  b 8
  c 7
  d 30
  e Answer should include the fact that pupils switched from choosing numbers in the middle of the range to numbers at the ends.
9 a 4
  b Answer should mention that nothing is known about the number of customers at times between the plotted points. There may have been times when there were no customers.
10 a 800 000
  b 300 000
  c 1980
  d 40 (accept any answer between 36 and 46)
11 a Diesel
  b 2010 and 2011
  c 2009
12 a 23
  b 5
  c 2
  d Week 4
  e 9
13 a Learn to drive (largest angle)
  b Learn self-defence (same angle as 'Learn to dance')
  c 9 × 6 = 54
14 a 42
  b 21
  c 7
15 a £90
  b £45
  c £60
16 a July
  b December
  c April
  d 11
  e The expected answer is No. Answer should include: according to the chart, most umbrellas are sold in the months that are summer in Northern Hemisphere and fewest in the winter months. This does not fit the usual weather pattern for the UK.
17 a 10°C
  b 8 am and 6 pm
  c 30°C
  d 22°C ± 1°C
18 a 2012
  b The 3rd quarter
  c 250
19 a 45
  b 55
20 a 4
  b 3
  c

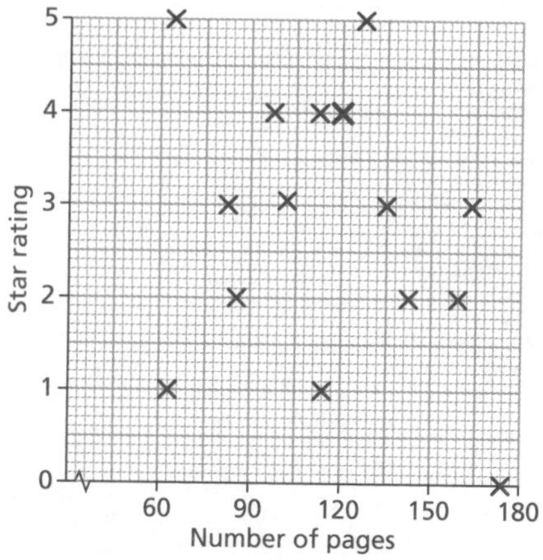

Star rating
0 1 2 3 4 5
60 90 120 150 180
Number of pages

d 3 stars

21 a 8 seconds

b 11

4.3 Find totals and modes from frequency tables or diagrams

1 a 25

b

Goals scored (G)	Frequency (F)	G × F
1	5	5
2	8	16
3	6	18
4	4	16
5	2	10
Totals	25	65

Total number of goals scored = 65

2

Number of strawberries (S)	Frequency (F)	S × F
10	1	10
11	3	33
12	11	132
13	9	117
14	4	56
15	2	30
Totals	30	378

a Number of punnets = 30

b Total number of strawberries = 378

3

Number of people (P)	Frequency (F)	P × F
1	32	32
2	21	42
3	12	36
4	8	32
5	3	15
	76	157

a There were 76 cars in the survey

b The total number of people was 157

4 a 58

b 1663

5 3

6 Pop

7 a 20

b 48

c 2

8 a 94

b 240

c 2

4.4 Describe correlation in scatter graphs

1 The scatter diagram shows negative correlation. As the distance from the centre increases, the number of crimes decreases.

2 There is no correlation. There is no clear connection between the heights of students and their maths scores.

3 There is a weak positive correlation between the maths and physics scores. As the maths scores increase the physics scores tend to increase.

4.5 Identify trends in time-series graphs

1 a The graph shows an upward trend in profits between 2010 and 2012.

b Answer should include: the graph continues the same trend; profits have nearly doubled since the new boss joined the company but there is no evidence that he has made a difference.

2 a The graph shows a downward trend in the number of arrests.

b Possible reasons include: greater police presence; the effect of an advertising campaign; stricter controls on the sale of alcohol.

3 a A strong upward trend.

b Overall, a strong upward trend but not consistently.

c 1990. A house bought at this time lost a lot of its value over the following 5 years.

4.6 Compare data

1 a Wednesday total = 34; Saturday total = 57

b 57 − 34 = 23

c i Ready salted

ii One possibility is that the shop sold out of Ready salted crisps.

2 a UK total = 83; Spain total = 126

b 43

c June

d August

3 a 12

b 21 pairs

c 22

d Fewer helmets: possibly because there are fewer motorcyclists on the road in January than in April. More gloves: possibly because people buy gloves in the winter even if they don't ride a motorbike.

4 a Tom's total number of shots is 32. Tom's mean number of shots is 32 ÷ 8 = 4.
Tom has a smaller mean number of shots than Jerry.
Tom's range is 6 − 1 = 5.
Tom's range is greater than Jerry's.

b Tom won the game. He had the smaller mean, so took fewer shots.

c Jerry was more consistent since he had the smaller range.

5 a Sara's total number of runs is 130.
Sara's mean score is 130 ÷ 3 = 26 runs.
Sara's mean score is less than Elise's.
Sara's range is 44 − 10 = 34. This is more than Elise's range.

b Elise has more runs since she has the higher mean score on the same number of matches.

c Elise is the more consistent player since she has the smaller range.

6 a The total amount that Fran received in tips was £30
The mean amount Fran received per day was £30 ÷ 5 = £6
Fran had a slightly larger mean than Megan.
The range of the amounts Fran received was £12 − 2 = £10.
This is more than Megan's range.

b Fran received more tips for the week since she had the greater mean for the same number of days.

c Fran's tips were more variable since her range was greater than Megan's.

7 a Putting Steve's results in order: 2, 3, 5, 6, 11.
The median distance for Steve was 5 m. This is less than Sheryl's median.
Steve's range was 11 − 2 = 9 m. This is more than Sheryl's range.

b Sheryl achieved the most consistent results since she had the smaller range.

8 a Putting the Passquick results in order: 24, 26, 27, 28, 30, 32, 40, 48.
The median number of lessons for Passquick is (28 +30) ÷ 2 = 29 lessons. This is slightly less than the median for Passmaster.
The range for Passquick is 48 − 24 = 24 lessons. This is more than the range for Passmaster.

b Answer should include: statement of decision about which company to use; comparison of the medians and comparison of the range values; comment about which of these comparisons has the bigger influence on your decision in this case.

9 1 Lizzy has a median score of 7.5 which is smaller than Sam's.
2 Lizzy's range is 10 − 7 = 3 which is smaller than Sam's.

10 a The modal height of the Cobras team is 188 cm. This is smaller than the modal height of the Bulldogs team. The range of the heights of the Cobras team is 192 − 185 = 7 cm. This is smaller than the range for the Bulldogs team.

b The team that is more consistent in height is the Cobras team since they have the smaller range.

11 The mode of Robin's scores is 9. Robin and Marion have the same mode.
The range of Robin's scores is 10 − 7 = 3.
Marion's lowest score is 8 and her maximum score can't be more than 10.
The range of Marion's scores is 2 or 1.
Marion's range is smaller than Robin's.
Marion is the winner.

12 a The mode of the given list of data is 9 which is less than the mode for the opposite direction. The range of the given list of data is 12 − 7 = 5. This is the same as for the opposite direction.

b One possibility is that the lights may be set to allow for greater flow of traffic in one direction at a particular time of day. For example, there is generally more traffic entering a city on a weekday morning than there is leaving it.

4.7 Make comparisons and predictions from data and representations of data

1 a Answer should include: David's team won most of the games that they played; the angle of the sector for 'Won' is the largest.
b Answer should include: it is not true; the total angle of the sectors for 'Lost' and 'Drawn' is larger than the angle for 'Won'.
c Calvin's team lost more matches.
d Answer should include: Calvin's team won more matches. Although the angle for 'Won' is bigger on David's chart, it isn't *twice* as big as the angle for 'Won' on Calvin's chart. It would need to be more than twice as big to represent more matches than Calvin's team won because Calvin's team played twice as many matches.

2 a Answer should include: Year 9 students over-estimated the proportion of Year 11 students starting work. Comparing the sectors in the two charts, 'Work' is larger in the Year 9 estimates than the actual results. The other sectors are smaller in the Year 9 estimates than the actual results.
b $140 \div 4 = 35$
c College

3 a Normal or underweight
b Obese
c Answer should include: the average weight of adult Americans has increased significantly; the obese category has gone from being the smallest to the largest; the normal or underweight category has gone from being the largest to the smallest.

4 a The US
b 2004
c 2008
d 2008 and 2009

5 a 7°C
b August
c 3°C
d 15°C
e Answer should include: Ko Samui; the temperatures in Ko Samui change very little – there is a level trend between October and December; the temperatures in Dubai are not so consistent; there is a downward trend between August and December; it is warmer in Ko Sumai than in Dubai in December; the temperature is likely to be higher in Ko Sumai than in Dubai in January.

6 a There was an upward trend.
b There was a downward trend.
c In Yorkshire there was a very slight downward trend in house prices. In London there was an upward trend.

7 Approximately 100 crimes

8 Approximately 60 marks

9 Approximately 15 seconds

10

11

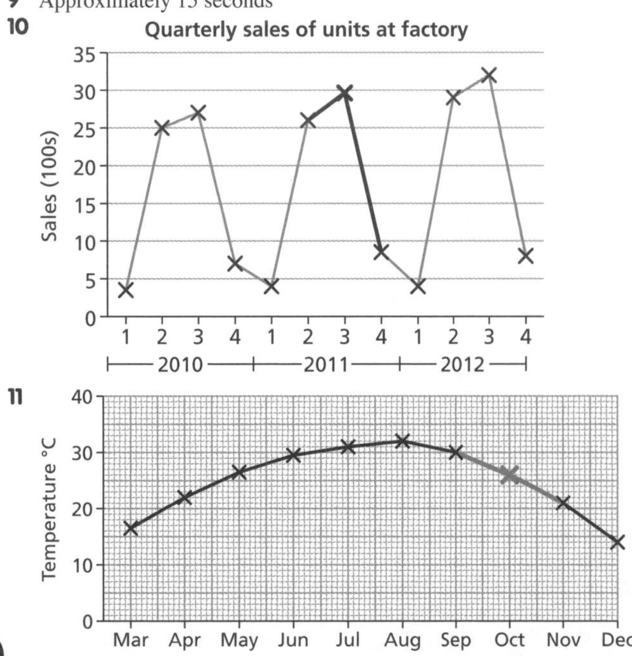

12

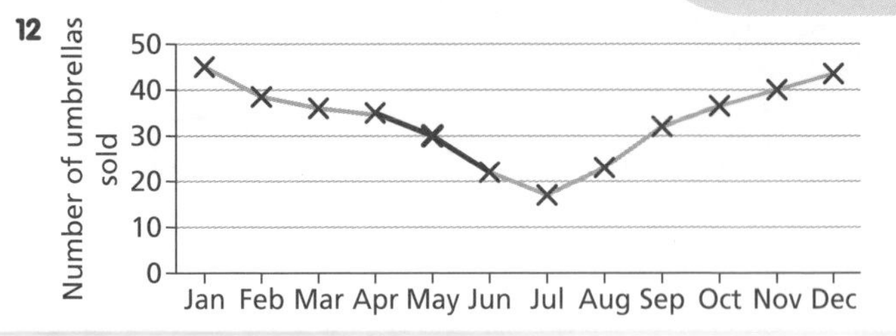

Don't forget!

* title
* pattern
* positive, * negative, * no correlation
* total
* highest
* time-series
* range
* proportions
* time
* time-series

Exam-style questions

1 a Missing values are: Germany 11 Gold; Republic of Korea 7 Bronze; Great Britain 65 total; United States of America 104 total.
b The order is decided on the number of Gold medals won. Great Britain won more Gold medals than the Russian Federation.
c 16

2 a 235 miles
b Bristol
c 293 miles

3 a 600
b

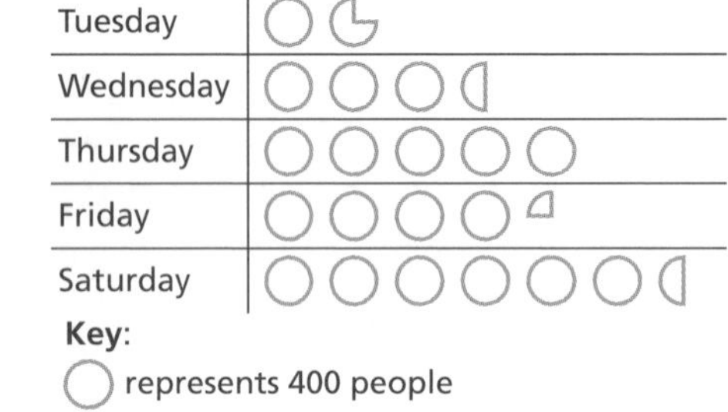

c 300

4 a Cycling
b Taekwondo
c 20

5 a Missing value: 3
b 3
c 4

6 a Strong positive
b Approximately 5 m

7 a

Number of cans	Frequency	Number of cans × Frequency
1	0	0
2	1	2
3	3	9
4	4	16
5	8	40
6	10	60
	26	127

a 26
b 10
c 127

8 Comparisons could include: a higher percentage of students gain a grade C or better in English than in maths; both subjects show an upward trend in the results; the upward trend in maths is slightly greater than in English so that the gap has narrowed.

9 A Positive; B No correlation; C Strong negative; D Weak negative

5 Probability

5.1 Use and interpret a probability scale

1 **b** Unlikely
c Certain
d Impossible
2 **a** Likely
b Evens
c Unlikely
3 **a** C
b A
c A
d B
4
B A C
0 0.5 1
5
B A D C
0 0.5 1

5.2 Write down theoretical and experimental probabilities

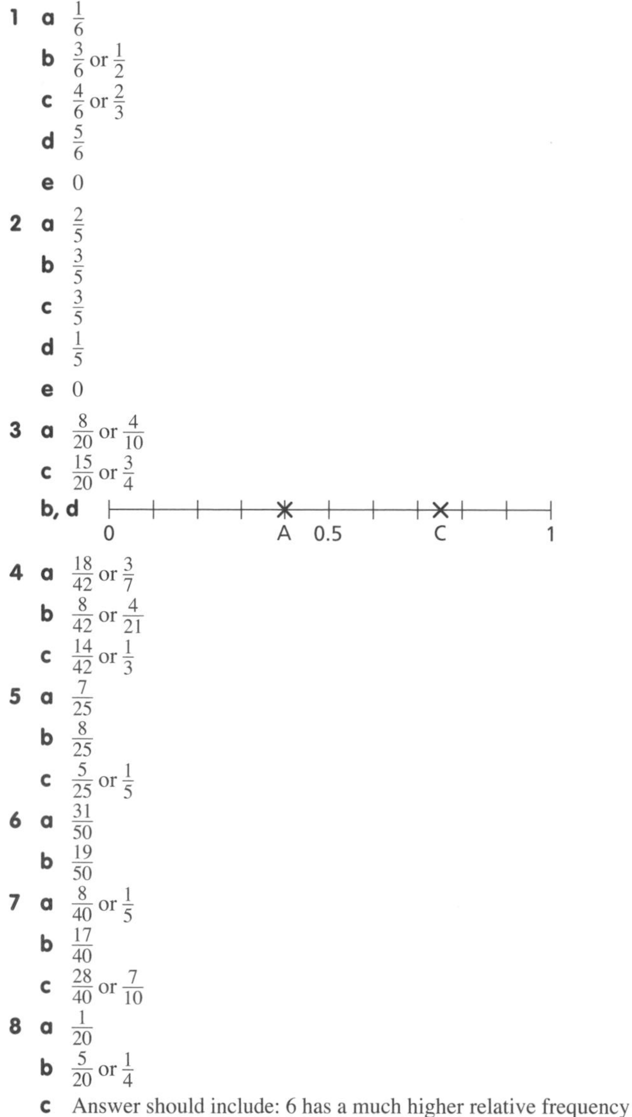

1 **a** $\frac{1}{6}$
b $\frac{3}{6}$ or $\frac{1}{2}$
c $\frac{4}{6}$ or $\frac{2}{3}$
d $\frac{5}{6}$
e 0
2 **a** $\frac{2}{5}$
b $\frac{3}{5}$
c $\frac{3}{5}$
d $\frac{1}{5}$
e 0
3 **a** $\frac{8}{20}$ or $\frac{4}{10}$
c $\frac{15}{20}$ or $\frac{3}{4}$
b, d
0 A 0.5 C 1
4 **a** $\frac{18}{42}$ or $\frac{3}{7}$
b $\frac{8}{42}$ or $\frac{4}{21}$
c $\frac{14}{42}$ or $\frac{1}{3}$
5 **a** $\frac{7}{25}$
b $\frac{8}{25}$
c $\frac{5}{25}$ or $\frac{1}{5}$
6 **a** $\frac{31}{50}$
b $\frac{19}{50}$
7 **a** $\frac{8}{40}$ or $\frac{1}{5}$
b $\frac{17}{40}$
c $\frac{28}{40}$ or $\frac{7}{10}$
8 **a** $\frac{1}{20}$
b $\frac{5}{20}$ or $\frac{1}{4}$
c Answer should include: 6 has a much higher relative frequency than 5; however, 20 is a small number of trials so the results are unreliable.
d Megan should carry out a lot more trials to make her results more reliable.

5.3 Estimate probabilities from practical situations

1 0.7875
2 0.6
3 **a** $\frac{21}{35}$ or $\frac{3}{5} = 0.6$
b 60%
4 **a** $\frac{66}{75}$ or $\frac{22}{25} = 0.88$
b 88%
c Answer should mention reliability of results based on the number of trials. Perhaps the other surgeon had only done one operation and that was successful.

5.4 Add probabilities

1 $0.25 + 0.45 = 0.7$; $1 - 0.7 = 0.3$. The probability that the spinner lands on blue is 0.3.
2 $1 - \frac{7}{11} = \frac{11}{11} - \frac{7}{11} = \frac{4}{11}$.
The probability that my team doesn't win on Saturday is $\frac{4}{11}$.
3 **a** $0.1 + 0.1 + 0.2 + 0.3 + 0.2 = 0.9$; $1 - 0.9 = 0.1$.
The probability of scoring 6 is 0.1.
b 4
c $0.2 + 0.3 = 0.5$
d $1 - 0.1 = 0.9$
4 0.3
5 **a** $\frac{3}{9}$ or $\frac{1}{3}$
b $\frac{7}{9}$
6 **a** 0.15
b 0.68
7 **a** 0.25
b 0.85
c 0.3

5.5 List outcomes

2 1, 2, 3, 4, 5, 6
3 red, red, yellow, yellow, yellow
4 blue, blue, green, green, green, green
5 red, white, blue
6 1, 2, 3, 4
7 H1, H2, H3, H4, H5, H6; T1, T2, T3, T4, T5, T6
8 HH, HT, TH, TT
9 SB, SR, SW; EB, ER, EW; HB, HR, HW
10 QX, QY, WX, WY, EX, EY, RX, RY
11 (A, 1), (A, 2), (A, 3), (B, 1), (B, 2), (B, 3), (C, 1), (C, 2), (C, 3),

Don't forget!

* outcomes
* 0
* 0, 1
* the event, number of outcomes
* The total number of trials
* increased
* different
* 1
* the event will occur
* sample space

Exam-style questions

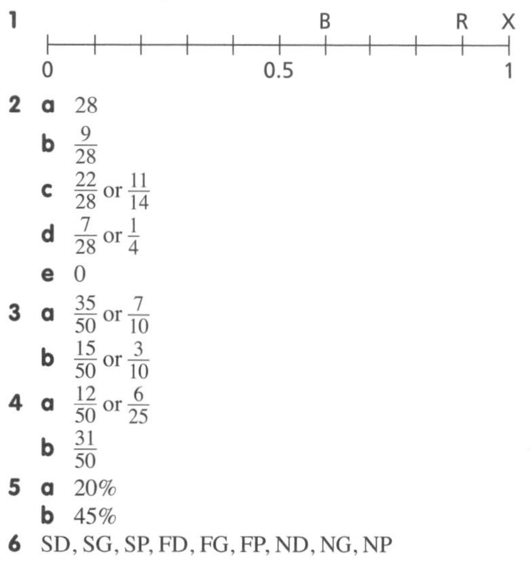

1
B R X
0 0.5 1
2 **a** 28
b $\frac{9}{28}$
c $\frac{22}{28}$ or $\frac{11}{14}$
d $\frac{7}{28}$ or $\frac{1}{4}$
e 0
3 **a** $\frac{35}{50}$ or $\frac{7}{10}$
b $\frac{15}{50}$ or $\frac{3}{10}$
4 **a** $\frac{12}{50}$ or $\frac{6}{25}$
b $\frac{31}{50}$
5 **a** 20%
b 45%
6 SD, SG, SP, FD, FG, FP, ND, NG, NP

Practice Paper

1 a Show for Wednesday on the pictogram.
b 264

2 a Totals are: Level 4: 88; Level 5: 219; Level 6: 176; Level 7: 54; Level 8: 18
b 219
c 85

3
B A C
0 $\frac{1}{2}$ 1

4 Data should be grouped, but different intervals may be used.

Number of letters	Tally	Frequency
0–5		
6–10		
11–15		
16–20		
21–25		
26–30		

5 a Jack
b 25
c 8
d 238

6 a 1 kg
b 2.5 kg
c 2.2 kg
d 5 kg

7 a

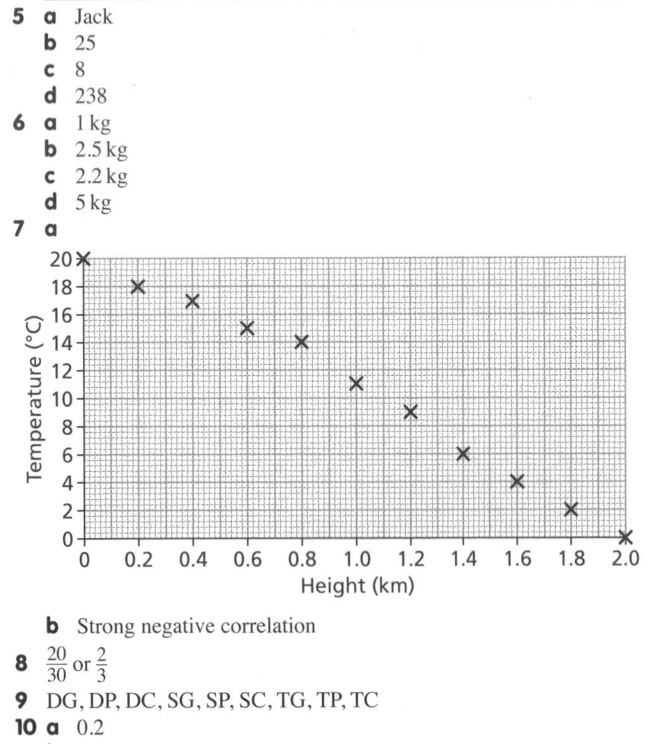

b Strong negative correlation

8 $\frac{20}{30}$ or $\frac{2}{3}$

9 DG, DP, DC, SG, SP, SC, TG, TP, TC

10 a 0.2
b 0.7
c 0.9

11 a dog
b 5
c 2
d dog

12 1 The choices overlap at 10 and 15.
2 There is no option for fewer than 5.
3 The question doesn't specify the time period for the practice to take place, e.g. in 1 week.

13 a 32
b 8
c 51

14 a Missing values are 9.84 (1996) and 9.69 (2008).
b 1984
c 9.63
d There is a downward trend in the times.

15 a $\frac{4}{10}$ or $\frac{2}{5}$ or 0.4
b The estimate is not reliable because the number of trials is too small. The reliability could be improved by increasing the number of trials.

16 Dan's mean score = 299 ÷ 10 = 29.9 and his range is 57 − 3 = 54. Dan has the higher mean score. He also has the greater range which suggests that he isn't as consistent as Rob.

17 1 The 3D effect makes it difficult to compare the heights of the bars.
2 The vertical scale doesn't start from 0 which makes comparisons difficult.
3 It isn't clear what the numbers on the vertical scale represent. It could be hundreds of thousands or even millions.

18 a

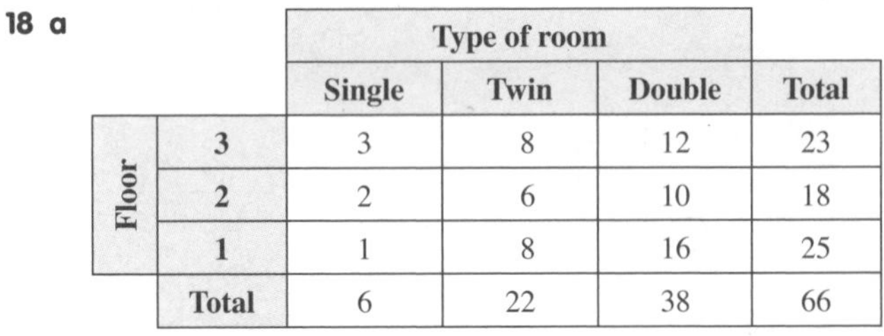

		Type of room			
		Single	Twin	Double	Total
Floor	3	3	8	12	23
	2	2	6	10	18
	1	1	8	16	25
	Total	6	22	38	66

b 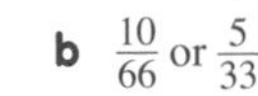 $\frac{10}{66}$ or $\frac{5}{33}$

19

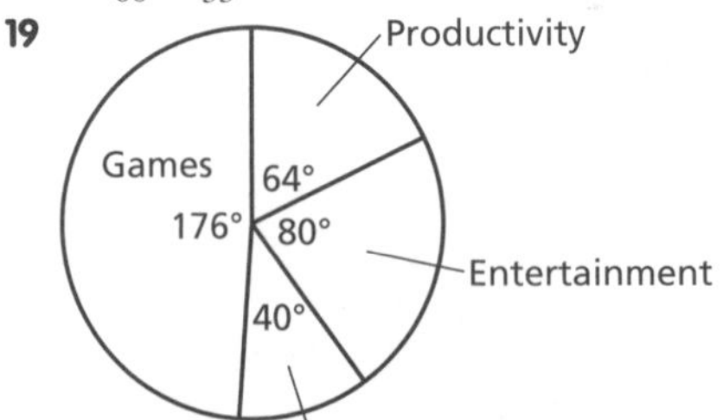

20

Length (l m)	Tally	Frequency
$0.90 < l \leq 1.00$	IIII	4
$1.00 < l \leq 1.10$	𝍸I	6
$1.10 < l \leq 1.20$	𝍸II	7
$1.20 < l \leq 1.30$	𝍸 𝍸	10
$1.30 < l \leq 1.40$	III	3

21 Missing number in table is 2. Total = 60

22 a Desktop computer
b 7
c 24